Beryllium

EVALUATION OF DEPOSITS DURING PROSPECTING AND EXPLORATORY WORK

A. A. Beus
ACADEMY OF SCIENCE, MOSCOW, THE USSR

Edited by LINCOLN R. PAGE
UNITED STATES GEOLOGICAL SURVEY

Translated by F. LACHMAN
for the U. K. ATOMIC ENERGY AUTHORITY

Preliminary Editing by R. K. HARRISON
ATOMIC ENERGY DIVISION
GEOLOGICAL SURVEY OF GREAT BRITAIN

PUBLICATION ARRANGED BY THE GEOCHEMICAL SOCIETY

W. H. Freeman and Company

SAN FRANCISCO AND LONDON

This book was first published in Moscow, in 1956, under the title Бериллий — оценка месторождений при поисках и разведках by Gosgeoltekhizdat, the State Publishing Office of Scientific and Technical Literature on Geology and Protection of Mineral Resources.

At the request of the author the original Chapter 3 has been replaced by the article, Geochemistry of Beryllium, published in *Geokhimiya*, No. 5, pp. 75–92, 1956.

Library of Congress Catalog Card Number 62-13299

Author's Foreword to the Russian Edition

It is not the purpose of this publication to develop formulae for a well-defined evaluation of beryllium deposits. Such evaluation is possible only if one has previously carried out a detailed study of the deposit including all of the complex factors governing the mode of origin of beryllium-bearing units and if one has reached an understanding of the regularities of concentrations of rare elements, including beryllium.

In each specific case, the evaluation of beryllium deposits should allow for all geological and mineralogical-chemical peculiarities of the deposit revealed during the prospecting and exploratory work.

The aim of this publication is to make a generalization of Soviet and foreign experience gained in studies of beryllium deposits and to establish the most efficient methods of prospection and evaluation.

Owing to the extraordinary scarcity of material relating to the geology, mineralogy, and geochemistry of beryllium deposits, this publication includes brief summaries of all available relevant data in the literature as well as the results of the author's investigations.

As the problem under consideration is both new and complicated, the author has been unable to avoid some shortcomings in presenting the material: any critical observations he receives from exploration and prospection geologists, for whose use this book is intended, will be greatly appreciated.

A. A. BEUS

Editor's Note

Many of the terms used by the author, such as "block microline," "paragenesis," "zone," and "replacement complex," when translated, tend to have a somewhat different meaning from that in common use by students of beryllium deposits in the Western world. These differences in meaning, for the most part, are self evident and, where possible, have been retained to avoid distorting the author's opinions and interpretations. His interpretations of pegmatites, described by geologists in the United States, are a case in point, because he does not mention the quite divergent hypotheses of origin held by those who personally studied these deposits.

March 1962   LINCOLN R. PAGE

Contents

PART I | Occurrence
Minerals
Geochemistry
Deposits

C H A P T E R | 1

Beryllium in Foreign Countries

Fields of Application and Economics of Beryllium Raw Material

In 1797, the French chemist, Vauquelin, discovered a new "earth," i.e. the oxide of an unknown chemical element, and called it the beryl earth.

In 1798, because of the sweet taste of its salts, the element of this oxide was called glucinium. It is only in France that this name has survived up to the present; in other countries the element is called beryllium, a name introduced by Klaproth.

Beryllium metal was obtained in 1828, but its production on an industrial scale began in 1921. Until the 'forties of the present century, the use and manufacture of beryllium could be expressed by very small figures. However, the development of engineering and the growing demand for materials with new properties, especially during recent years, were the cause of a considerable increase in the consumption of beryllium, in the form of compounds, alloys, and other articles made from this metal.

For this reason the principal capitalist countries began to widen considerably the scope of geological exploration and scientific research work, the aim of which was to locate, study, and exploit beryllium deposits.

3

The discovery of properties of beryllium useful in the generation of atomic energy, within a short time, increased still more the demand for beryllium ores and occasioned a further increase of scientific and geological exploration work in this field. The fundamental aim of this task, viz. the preparation of an ore production program which would guarantee a sufficient supply of beryllium for the growing industrial needs and to set up State reserves of beryllium ores, is solved in various ways:

1. by intensive exploration and exploitation of known deposits in which beryllium is present as the main useful element or as the usable by-product;

2. by prospecting for new beryllium deposits;

3. by an inspection of all previously known beryllium deposits in order to determine the possibility of economical extraction of beryllium;

4. by exploring possibilities of utilizing new types of beryllium ore.

On the basis of data published in foreign publications (Minerals Yearbook, 1940–1952), the consumption of beryllium increased fivefold during the second world war. In the post-war period the production of beryllium concentrate has kept on increasing, and has already exceeded 9000 tons yearly (Table 1).

Beryllium is used at present in many different fields; of particularly wide application are the so-called beryllium bronzes, endowed with great hardness, strength, and resistance to corrosion, which enable them to be used for making reliable components in a number of modern mechanisms exposed to protracted and intensive stresses.

The principal fields of the application of beryllium in the industry of foreign countries are listed below.

Beryllium Metal

1. X-ray tube windows with a penetrability greatly exceeding that of other metals (e.g., their penetrability is 17 times as great as that of aluminum windows).

2. As a neutron source and moderator in nuclear industry.

3. Casehardening of articles with beryllium to impart a high surface hardness.

Beryllium-copper Alloys (Beryllium Bronzes)

1. Spiral and leaf springs for particularly stressed parts of machines, weapons, and instruments.

2. Parts of aircraft undercarriage.

3. Casings and parts of instruments whose strength should equal that of steel, but which should have no magnetic properties (should not be capable of magnetization).

Table 1 | *Production of beryllium concentrate[1] (in tons)*

COUNTRIES	1939	1943	1946	1947	1948	1949	1950	1951	1952	1953
Estimated grand total in capitalist countries	904	5452	1700	1430	2470	4587	6651	5720	6530	9250
Including:										
Brazil (export)	504	2027	1294	1027	1783	3078	2625	1533	2533	3000
Argentina	299	881	130	10	50[2]	—	—	—	498[3]	1365
U.S.A. (mine shipments)	86	323	91	132	90	431	507	439	467	681
Morocco				---	51	211	56	84	129	33
Madagascar		67		—	9	27	486	530	395	312
Mozambique		6	22	81	16	136	264	230	140	218
Southern Rhodesia			—	—	—	23	846	1007	1076	1596
Uganda		—	—	18	44	34	71	2	3	32
South-West Africa	—	36	5	52	90	239	659	753	536	535
Union of South Africa	—	78	—	—	—	223	844	593	375	478
Portugal		14	—	—	10	3	52	102	78	378
India	9	1486	112	—	—	—	—	215	—	—
Australia	6	534	19	54	56	36	23	114	91	127

[1] Mainly hand-sorted lump concentrate (except U.S.A.) containing 10–12 percent beryllium oxide.

[2] Lump and flotation concentrates containing 10–12 percent beryllium oxide.

[3] Imported by the U.S.A. from Argentina.

4. Ball-races, bearings, and bushings in machine parts exposed to intensive stress and friction.

5. Striking pins in quick-firing automatic weapons, particularly those used in aircraft.

6. Contact brushes and other electrical contacts.

7. Non-sparking (safety) instruments used in industries liable to fire hazard, e.g., in the manufacture of explosives, etc.

Beryllium Compounds (Oxide and Salts)

1. Mixtures of beryllium salts are used in the preparation of beryllium-containing luminescent compounds (luminophors) which possess very advantageous light characteristics.

2. Beryllium oxide is used as heat-resisting material with a low electrical conductivity for special electro-radio insulators, and as a chemically passive and highly heat-resisting material in metallurgical engineering.

As mentioned in numerous foreign economic surveys, this wide utilization of beryllium in industry has been limited up to now by the scarcity and high price

of the beryllium raw material, of beryllium compounds and alloys, and of
beryllium metal. In addition, there are great technical difficulties in obtaining
these products in the high degree of purity indispensable to modern engineering.

By far the most important consumer and importer of beryllium and beryllium
concentrates among capitalist countries is the U.S.A. (Table 2).

Table 2 | *Imports of beryllium concentrates into U.S.A. (in tons)*

COUNTRIES	1946	1947	1948	1949	1950	1951	1952	1953
Argentina	48	—	50	—	—	—	499	1372
Australia	18	40	—	—	—	—	—	—
Brazil	903	655	1400	2960	2451	992	2349	2445
British East Africa	—	—	—	10	10	43	16	23
Morocco	—	—	—	20	70	21	107	24
India	108	—	—	—	—	—	—	—
Japan	—	—	—	97	15	11	—	—
Mozambique	—	—	50	97	118	158	279	372
Portugal	—	—	—	—	25	88	95	342
Southern Rhodesia	—	—	—	—	420	627	844	1164
Union of South Africa (including South-West Africa)	—	—	43	263	1270	1562	1048	1242
Other countries	—	—	17	9	27	411	184	493
Total	1077	695	1560	3456	4406	3913	5421	7477

It can be seen from Table 1 that the countries with beryllium deposits are
spread all over the world, but it should be mentioned that the number of
deposits of commercial importance is very limited. Moreover, we lack reliable
data regarding ore reserves, even in the case of areas which are considered at
present to be the main sources of beryllium raw material (the states of Paraiba
and Rio Grande do Norte in Brazil, South Africa, India, etc.). The reserves of
extractable beryl in the U.S.A., as calculated in 1952, were of the order of
15,000 tons and the total world reserves of beryl (except the USSR and
Communist China), as estimated by American experts (President's Materials
Policy Commission), were 185,000 tons.

The scarcity of beryl ores, which manifested itself soon after the beginning of
the second world war and became more and more acute as the demand for
beryllium increased, induced a number of States to adopt special measures for
promoting mining and for establishing State reserves of beryl ores.

Thus, late in 1946 India prohibited beryl exports. France allowed the export
of beryl from Madagascar, only to metropolitan France. Towards the end of

the second world war Germany had about 500 tons of beryllium in reserve stores (A large part of these reserves was seized by France.).

According to the order dated June 1, 1942, the U.S. Office of War Production subjected the sale of beryllium of any type to government control. In June, 1948, the U.S. Government banned the exports of beryllium concentrates and ores from the U.S.A. without special licenses (with the exception of Canada). One can expect, according to the report of the Materials Policy Commission (1952), submitted to the President of the U.S.A., "that, by 1975, the demand for beryllium ore in the U.S.A. will increase roughly $2\frac{1}{2}$ times that of 1950. At the same time mining in the U.S.A. will probably be able to satisfy only a small part of the demand, and by 1975 its yield will probably amount to 15% of the imports."

Consumption of Beryllium
Concentrates in the U.S.A.

Year	Tons
1936	180
1937	180
1939	270
1941	1100
1943	2752
1947	1562
1948	1188
1949	933
1950	2727
1951	3073
1952	3153
1953	2414

It should be noted that the great increase of beryllium ore imports into the U.S.A. is the result of special steps taken by the U.S. Government which, treating these imports as a matter of top priority, placed at their disposal all means of transport (including aircraft) for bringing in beryl from far-off countries.

It has been noted already that, as regards beryllium, the commercial conditions which emerged during and after the war brought about an intensification of prospecting for, and exploration of, new beryllium deposits, and the resumption of mining beryllium ores in old, abandoned mines. One of the clear examples of how the capitalist industrial circles reacted to the commercial conditions referred to above was the decision (taken in March, 1946) by Beryl Mining Co. Ltd. (South Africa) to raise the share capital from £40,000 to

£100,000. While announcing at the annual shareholders' meeting that mining of beryl had been resumed on a large scale in one of the oldest South African mines (Somerset mine), the chairman of the Board justified this decision by the large demand for beryl on the part of the consumers' concerns which expressed their readiness to buy all of the mined beryl concentrate, even the low-grade material. Beryl mining was resumed also in many old mines in the U.S.A., which previously had been abandoned because the extraction of beryl ceased to be a paying proposition (a number of deposits in the Black Hills area, etc.).

The increase in beryl mining was stimulated by the continuous increase in prices of beryllium concentrates; this can be seen in Table 3.

Table 3 | *Increase of purchase price of beryllium concentrates in the U.S.A. (in U.S. dollars)*

YEAR	1939	1940	1941	1942	1943	1947	1948	1949
Mean price of 1% beryllium oxide in one metric ton of concentrate	3.49	3.27	5.95	7–8	8.6–9	17.6–19.8	26.4–28.6 (imported 24–25)	28.6–33 (imported 26–29.4)

The need for considerably increasing the output of beryllium raw materials brought about the development of wide-scale scientific research work, both in the U.S.A. and in other countries, the purpose of which was to utilize new sources of beryllium raw materials.

This work may be subdivided into several categories:

1. prospection and examination of the deposits of phenacite and other beryllium minerals (helvite, chrysoberyl, euclase, bertrandite, etc.);

2. development of methods of beneficiation of disseminated beryl ores;

3. development of methods of beneficiation and of technological processing for helvite ores.

It should be noted that to date no favorable results have been obtained abroad in prospecting for phenacite in worthwhile concentrations.

Notwithstanding the discouraging results of investigations carried out up to now, geological exploration is still being conducted in the U.S.A., not only of the deposits of macrocrystalline beryl, but also of the deposits of disseminated beryllium ores, e.g., helvite, and in the deposits of microcrystalline beryl and other beryllium minerals. Special attention is paid to the by-production of beryl from complex deposits of rare metals, mica, and ceramic raw materials.

Besides geological exploration work, we witness in the U.S.A. a detailed study of methods of technological processing and beneficiation of various types of beryllium ores.

It is pointed out in the literature that favorable results have not yet been attained in the field of beneficiation of the helvite ores. At the same time the problem of beneficiation of disseminated beryl ores has been apparently solved to a certain extent in the U.S.A. The daily press contains a mention of the erection of the first beneficiation plant on the site of bervl ore deposits in the U.S.A. near Gunnison, Colo.

Requirements of Industry Regarding the Quality of Beryllium Raw Material

Until quite recently foreign countries have used exclusively macrocrystalline beryl ores capable of beneficiation by hand picking. In this method the minimum size of the extracted beryl grains is limited to +5 cm.

As far as one can see from the data of foreign sources, the industrial minimum beryl content in ores is variable depending on a number of economic factors, the most important of which are: the demand for this raw material, the cost of labor in the given area, and the possibility of total exploitation of the deposit.

The exploitation of a deposit is usually considered to be economic if the content of pickable beryl exceeds 0.2 percent. In countries, however, where labor wages are extremely low (Brazil, South-West Africa, Portuguese East Africa, etc.), or whenever total exploitation of the deposit is feasible, ores with a lower beryl content are also worked.

The beryl concentrates supplied to the beryllium processing industry are at present almost exclusively a product of hand picking of the beryl and contain, depending on the varieties of beryl and on the degree of contamination of its crystals by inclusions of extraneous minerals, 8–13 percent of beryllium oxide. The overall chemical composition of concentrates practically corresponds with the composition of beryl, there being insignificant oscillations because of impurities. In connection with the wide development in various countries of work on methods of mechanical beneficiation, including flotation of disseminated beryllium ores, one can expect that within the next few years the existing requirements of the industry with respect to beryllium concentrates will undergo a change and that methods of processing new types of beryllium ores will be developed.

Beryllium Minerals

Over 20 beryllium minerals are known in nature (Table 4): only five of them, however, may be considered to be more or less widespread (beryl, phenacite, chrysoberyl, bertrandite, and the minerals of the helvite-danalite series). The remaining beryllium minerals are either rare or very rare, and some, e.g., bromellite and barylite, are only known in two deposits on our globe.

The only mineral which, up to the present moment, has been of commercial importance as raw material for beryllium production, is beryl. As regards other beryllium minerals, of greatest interest are: phenacite, chrysoberyl, and the minerals of the helvite-danalite group.

Brief characteristics of the six most important beryllium minerals are given below.

Beryl, $Be_3Al_2[Si_6O_{18}]$

Physical, Optical, and Chemical Properties

Hexagonal symmetry. The crystal structure of beryl is highly characteristic, being determined by the presence of the $[Si_6O_{18}]$ rings which are bonded by the Be and Al ions arranged between them. The $[Si_6O_{18}]$ rings arranged one above another form an open channel which can accommodate the ions of the alkaline metals—sodium, potassium, lithium, caesium, and rubidium—and

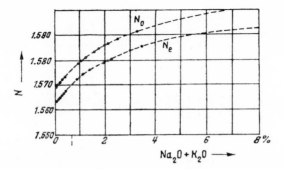

Fig. 1. Relationship between the refractive indices of beryl and its chemical composition (alkali-content) according to M. D. Dorfman (1952). Absicssae: to the left of mark —Greisens and hypothermal veins; to the right—Pegmatites.

H_2O and helium. The crystals are hexagonal prisms; depending on the peculiarities of chemical composition of the mineral the habit varies from long prisms in alkali-free varieties to short prisms and even a tabular habit in the case of the alkali-rich varieties. Hardness 7.5–8. Glassy luster. Imperfect cleavage; fracture uneven or conchoidal. Specific gravity 2.63–2.91. Specific gravity and refractive indices increase with the alkali content (Fig. 1). Optically uniaxial, negative. $\epsilon = 1.595 - 1.564$; $\omega = 1.568 - 1.602$; $\omega - \epsilon = 0.004 - 0.008$.

There are several varieties of beryl, depending on the nature of impurities and it should be noted, in the list below, that the composition of the impurities is usually determined by the conditions of mineral formation (Table 5).

BERYL FREE FROM ALKALIES (THE SUM OF THE ALKALIES IS LESS THAN 0.5 PERCENT)

1. Common beryl. Green or yellowish-green—pigmented by ferric iron. Widespread in unreplaced pegmatites, pneumatolytes, and quartz veins.

2. Aquamarine. Blue. In unreplaced pegmatites (commonly in druses), pneumatolytes, and quartz veins.

3. Heliodor. "Wine"-yellow—pigmented by ferric iron. In unreplaced pegmatites and pneumatolytes.

4. Emerald. Emerald-green—pigmented by chromium. In pegmatites of the crossing line.

The crystals have a long prismatic habit. As a rule, they are well formed.

ALKALI-CONTAINING BERYL (THE SUM OF THE ALKALIES EXCEEDS 0.5 PERCENT)

1. Sodium beryl ($Na_2O = 0.5–2$ percent; $Li_2O = 0.1–0.5$ percent). Pale-green, greenish-yellowish, greenish-white, or white. In fully-differentiated and

Table 4   *Properties of the most important beryllium minerals*

NAME	CHEMICAL COMPOSITION[1]	BeO CONTENT (IN %)	SYMMETRY	SPECIFIC GRAVITY	HARDNESS	COLOR	HABIT	PARAGENESIS
						OXIDES AND COMPOUND OXIDES		
Bromellite	BeO	98.02	Hexagonal.	3.02	9	White.	Small prismatic.	In calcite veins in hematitic skarns—with swedenborgite, richterite, manganophyllite.
Chrysoberyl	Al_2BeO_4	19.8	Orthorhombic.	3.50–3.84	8.5	Yellow, yellow-green, emerald-green (in alexandrite).	Thick tabular or short prismatic. Commonly pseudohexagonal, trillings are typical.	In pegmatites—with feldspars, chlorite, talc, muscovite, phlogopite, phenacite, beryl. In skarns—with fluorite, vesuvianite, helvite, phenacite, magnetite, etc.
						SILICATES		
Phenacite	$Be_2[SiO_4]$	45.5	Trigonal.	2.96–3.0	7.5	Colorless transparent, yellowish, brown.	Rhombohedral short-columnar to acicular and radiating.	Do.
Euclase	$AlBe[SiO_4](OH)$[1]	17.0–21.8	Monoclinic.	3.05–3.10	6.5–7	Colorless, pale-green, blue.	Prismatic, abounding in faces.	In veins in limestones or schists—with rock crystal, topaz, etc.
Bertrandite	$Be_4[Si_2O_7](OH)_2$	39.6–42.6	Orthorhombic.	2.59–2.60	6	Colorless, white, yellowish.	Prismatic or tabular.	In pegmatites and greisens—with beryl, muscovite, albite, topaz, quartz.
Barylite	$BaBe_2[Si_2O_7]$	16	Do.	4.0	7	Do.	Do.	In contact deposits of manganese and zinc.
Gadolinite	$(Y,Ca)_2Fe[BeSiO_4]_2(O,OH)_2$[1]	5.5–12.9	Monoclinic.	4.0–4.65	6.5–7	Brownish-black, greenish-black.	Irregular formations and solid masses.	In pegmatites—with biotite, fergusonite, allanite, etc.
Beryl	$Al_2Be_3[Si_6O_{18}]$	11–14.3	Hexagonal.	2.63–2.91	7.5–8	Blue, greenish-blue, green, yellow-green, yellow, brown, white, colorless, rose.	From prismatic to short-prismatic and tabular.	In pegmatites—with quartz, microcline, muscovite, albite, tantaloniobates, etc. In greisens and quartz veins—with quartz, muscovite, topaz, fluorite, wolframite, molybdenite, etc.
Milarite	$KCa_2(Be_2Al)[Si_{12}O_{30}]$[1]	5.2	Do.	2.55–2.59	5.5	Colorless, pale-green.	Prismatic.	In Alpine veins—with adularia, zeolites.

NAME	CHEMICAL COMPOSITION[1]	BeO CONTENT (IN %)	SYMMETRY	SPECIFIC GRAVITY	HARD-NESS	COLOR	HABIT	PARAGENESIS
Bavenite	$Ca_4[(Be,Al)_4Si_9(O,OH)_{26}](OH)_2$	6.3–7.7	Orthorhombic.	2.74	5.5	White.	Flat prismatic, in radiating aggregates.	In pegmatites and greisens—with beryl, as secondary mineral.
Eudidymite	$Na[BeSi_3O_7](OH)$[1]	10.5–11.2	Monoclinic.	2.54–2.55	6	Colorless, white.	Tabular.	In albitized nepheline syenite pegmatites.
Epididymite			Orthorhombic.		5.5			
Leucophanite	$Na_{0.6-1}Ca[BeSi_2O_6]$[1]	10–12	Orthorhombic.	2.96	4	White, yellowish, greenish.	Do.	In cavities of nepheline syenite pegmatites.
Meliphanite	$Fe_{0.6-1}Ca[BeSi_2O_6]$[1]	10–11	Tetragonal.	3.0	5–5.5	Yellow.	From tabular to short-prismatic.	Do.
Chkalovite	$Na_2[BeSi_2O_6]$	11.3–12.7	Orthorhombic.	2.6	6	Colorless, white.	Irregular monocrystal formations.	In nepheline syenite pegmatites—with ussingite, aegirine, schizolite, natrolite.
Helvite	$Mn_8[BeSiO_4]_6S_2$[1]	11–14.2	Cubic.	3.16–3.42	6–6.5	Yellow, brown, red, green, grey.	Tetrahedral.	In pegmatites—with albite. In skarns—with magnetite, fluorite.
Danalite	$Fe_8[BeSiO_4]_6S_2$[1]	12.7–14.7	Cubic.	3.35–3.43	5.5–6	Yellow, brown, red, green, grey.	Octahedral.	In pegmatites—with albite. In skarns—with magnetite, fluorite.
Genthelvite	$Zn_8[BeSiO_4]_6S_2$[1]	12.6	Do.	3.66	5.5–6	Do.	Do.	In nepheline syenite pegmatites.
					BORATES			
Hambergite	$Be_2[BO_3](OH)$	53.5	Orthorhombic.	2.35	7.5	White.	Prismatic.	In boron-rich pegmatites.
					PHOSPHATES			
Beryllonite	$NaBe[PO_4]$	19–20	Monoclinic.	2.8	5.5–6	Colorless, yellowish.	From short-columnar to tabular.	In albitized granitic pegmatites—with albite, triphylite, beryl, etc.
Hurlbutite	$CaBe_2[PO_4]$[1]	21.3	Orthorhombic.	2.88	6	Colorless, yellowish, greenish.	Irregular crystals.	Do.
Herderite	$CaBe[PO_4]\cdot(OH,F)$[1]	15–16	Monoclinic.	3.00	5	Do.	Prismatic.	Do.
Moraesite	$Be_2[PO_4](OH)4H_2O$	25–28	Do.	1.806	?	White.	Acicular.	In cavities of albitized pegmatites rich in phosphates, replaces beryl.

[1] Chemical formulae in this table were changed to agree with those listed in Chapter 3. *Ed.*

Table 5   *Typomorphic characteristics of beryl*

TYPE OF DEPOSIT	ZONES AND PARAGENETICAL COMPLEXES	VARIETY OF BERYL	SUM OF ALKALIES (IN %)	CRYSTAL FORM	COLOR	CHARACTERISTIC PARAGENESIS
Pegmatite.	Zone of block quartz (quartz core).	Without alkalies (ordinary beryl, aquamarine).	<0.5	Prismatic, commonly with "cap." Usually well-formed.	Green, bright-green, yellowish-green. Blue. From opaque to transparent.	Quartz, muscovite, macrocrystalline columbite-tantalite.
	Drusy cavities in the zone of block quartz.	Without alkalies (beryl, aquamarine, rarely heliodor).	<0.5	Do.	Do. (Rarely from wine-yellow to brown.)	Quartz (morion, rock crystal), microcline, bertrandite.
	Quartz-muscovite substituting complex.	Without alkalies, less often sodium beryl.	<0.5	Prismatic. Commonly poorly formed.	Green, bright-green, commonly semi-transparent.	Quartz, muscovite.
	Albite-muscovite substituting complex. Albitized portions in the zones of the block and apographic pegmatite.	Sodium beryl.	>0.5	Sharp-pyramidal (coniform), truncated-pyramidal. Usually poorly formed; sometimes irregular formations.	Yellowish-green, from bright-green to white.	Albite, muscovite, quartz, columbite-tantalite, triphylite.
	Zones: cleavelandite, cleavelandite-spodumene, and albite-lepidolite.	Sodium-lithium beryl (rosterite).	>1	Irregular formations, less frequently short-prismatic.	From white to water-clear.	Albite, spodumene, muscovite, lepidolite, columbite-tantalite, lithiophylite.
		Lithium-caesium beryl (vorobyevite, rosterite).	>1	From short-prismatic to tabular. Irregular formations.	From colorless to rose.	Do.
Hydro-thermal-pneumatolytic.	Quartz, quartz-feldspar veins, and greisen formations.	Without alkalies (ordinary beryl, aquamarine, heliodor).	<0.5	From bladed to prismatic. Radiating aggregates, dense granular masses.	Green of various hues, blue, yellow-brown.	Quartz, topaz, muscovite, fluorite.

block type, partly albitized pegmatites. Crystal habit prismatic, pyramidal, or short prismatic; usually poorly developed.

2. Sodium-lithium beryl (Li_2O = 0.5–1.5 percent; Na_2O = 1–2.5 percent). Greenish-white, white, or colorless. In replaced pegmatites. Crystal habit is short prismatic; frequently irregular.

3. Lithium-caesium beryl (Li_2O = 0.1–1 percent; Cs_2O < 3 percent; Na_2O = 0.3–1 percent). Colorless, pinkish-white, or pink. In replaced pegmatites with lepidolite. Crystal habit is short prismatic to tabular; commonly poorly formed.

The colorless variety of beryl, rosterite, may include both the lithium and the lithium-caesium variety. The latter includes also the rose-pink vorobyevite (morganite). Results of chemical analyses of the typical varieties of beryl are shown in Table 6.

Identification

Beryl usually can be identified readily owing to the characteristic hexagonal crystal form and to high hardness. However, in a number of places poorly developed crystals of the sodium and lithium beryl variety are outwardly difficult to distinguish from quartz. In such a case microchemical or optical methods must be used. In microchemical determination one uses the conventional spot reaction with quinalizarine, described in the literature (Barlow et al., 1955); in optical identification by immersion liquid the features distinguishing beryl from quartz are the former's higher refractive index and its negative optical sign.

It should be noted that each of the varieties referred to above is related to a definite stage of mineral formation; thus different generations of beryl are very characteristic typomorphic minerals of the pegmatitic and pneumatolytic processes.

Origin and Paragenesis

Beryl is equally characteristic of the pegmatite and of the hydrothermal-pneumatolytic deposits, and possesses a very wide crystallization interval and a wide range of varieties. Because beryl is the main commercial beryllium mineral, its deposits and paragenesis will be described in detail in Chapter 4, "Types of Beryllium Deposits."

Phenacite, Be₂[SiO₄]

Physical, Optical, and Chemical Properties

Trigonal symmetry. The crystal structure of phenacite is determined by the presence of independent [SiO₄] groups which are bonded by beryllium in such

Table 6   *Chemical composition of beryl varieties in percent*

OXIDES	EMERALD	HELIODOR	AQUA-MARINE (FROM GREISEN)	ALKALI-FREE BERYL	SODIUM BERYL (BRIGHT GREEN)	SODIUM BERYL (YELLOWISH-GREEN)	SODIUM BERYL (WHITE)	SODIUM-LITHIUM BERYL (WHITE)	CAESIUM BERYL (COLOR-LESS)	LITHIUM-CAESIUM BERYL (ROSE, TRANSPARENT VOROBYEVITE)
SiO_2	64.40	64.31	64.22	63.62	64.40	64.16	63.76	63.60	64.64	62.76
Al_2O_3	18.03	18.71	20.00	20.69	18.52	17.84	18.83	18.53	19.10	19.75
Fe_2O_3	0.50	0.64	0.20	0.31	0.35	0.84	0.37	0.16	0.14	0.06
Cr_2O_3	0.23	—	—	—	—	—	—	—	—	—
BeO	14.28	13.98	14.26	14.30	12.78	12.48	12.78	11.74	11.32	12.66
FeO	tr.	None.	0.10	—	None.	—	—	None.	tr.	—
MnO	0.19	0.008	—	—	0.13	0.21	0.10	0.07	—	0.05
MgO	0.52	0.08	0.13	tr.	0.20	0.28	0.24	0.18	—	tr.
CaO	0.16	0.18	0.46	None.	0.26	0.36	0.11	—	0.17	tr.
Li_2O	tr.	None.	None.	None.	—	—	—	0.78	0.31	0.83
Na_2O	0.48	tr.	None.	None.	0.91	1.54	1.76	2.43	tr.	1.27
K_2O	0.14	None.	None.	None.	—	—	—	—	1.42	—
Rb_2O	—	None.	None.	None.	0.05	0.19	0.44	0.44	1.72	1.14
Cs_2O	—	None.	None.	None.	—	—	—	—	1.21	1.35
H_2O^+	1.60	2.22	1.05	1.25	2.38	2.30	1.67	2.44	—	—
Sum Total	100.53	100.158	100.42	100.10	99.99	100.20	100.06	100.17	100.03	99.87

a way that every oxygen ion of the silicon-oxygen tetrahedron participates in two adjacent beryllium-oxygen tetrahedra. The elementary rhombohedral cell contains six $Be_2[SiO_4]$ molecules. Willemite has an analogous crystal structure. The crystal habit is different in deposits of different type, varying from rhombohedral to short-columnar and acicular. In metasomatic formations of the skarn type it is observed as extremely small radial concretions within fluorite. It is usually colorless, less frequently yellowish or rose. Luster glassy or greasy. Imperfect cleavage. Fracture from uneven to conchoidal. Hardness 7.5. Specific gravity 2.96–3.0. Optically uniaxial, positive: $\epsilon = 1.670$; $\omega = 1.654$: $\epsilon - \omega = 0.016$. Chemical composition: BeO 45.5 percent; SiO_2 54.5 percent.

Identification

Identified usually with difficulty. It differs from beryl by a higher refractive index and a positive optical sign, and from quartz by a higher refractive index and a higher specific gravity.

Origin and Paragenesis

It is related mainly to pegmatites of the crossing line and with metasomatic formations at the contact of beryllium-bearing granites with limestones, where it is formed under conditions of scarcity of Al_2O_3 and SiO_2. In the ordinary granitic pegmatites it occurs in cavities as the latest beryllium mineral. In places the formation of phenacite after helvite has been noted. Usual paragenesis: (1) in the crossing line pegmatites—with chlorite, phlogopite, oligoclase, fluorite, and chrysoberyl; (2) in the contact metasomatic formations—with fluorite, chrysoberyl, and sometimes magnetite and other skarn minerals; (3) in ordinary pegmatites—with albite, microcline, and beryl.

Chrysoberyl, Al₂BeO₄

Physical Properties

Orthorhombic symmetry. The crystal structure of chrysoberyl is analogous to that of forsterite, the positions of Mg and Si in the crystal lattice of forsterite corresponding with those of Al and Be respectively, in chrysoberyl. The oxygen ions have a denser packing, close to the hexagonal one; a sixfold co-ordination with respect to oxygen is characteristic of the aluminum ions and a fourfold co-ordination is characteristic of the beryllium ions. The crystal structure determines the great hardness and stability of the chrysoberyl crystals. The crystal habit is tabular (100), short-prismatic, and commonly pseudohexagonal. Trillings along (031) occur. Fine, irregular grains are characteristic of metasomatic formations (skarns). Color yellow, greenish-yellow, green. The chromium-containing precious variety, alexandrite, in artificial light can change from green to purple. Glassy luster. Cleavage along (010), (001), and (100) imperfect. Fracture from uneven to conchoidal. Brittle. Hardness 8.5. Specific gravity 3.50–3.75.

Optical Properties

The refractive indices vary even within the same crystal, obviously in connection with the content of Fe^{3+} and Cr. $\gamma = 1.753–1.758$; $\beta = 1.747–1.749$; $\alpha = 1.744–1.747$; $\gamma - \alpha = 0.009$. Pleochroism is usually weak in the yellowish-green varieties and strong for intensely-colored varieties; α-red; β-orange; γ-green. Optically biaxial, positive. 2V = 45–71°. Plane of optical axes (010).

Chemical Composition

BeO 19.8 percent, Al_2O_3 80.2 percent; there are always impurities: Fe_2O_3 (3.5–6 percent), sometimes TiO_2 (<3 percent), and Cr_2O_3 (<0.4 percent) which accounts for the emerald-green coloration of alexandrite. Most investigators consider that chrysoberyl is a compound Be and Al oxide. On the basis of crystal structure it can be analyzed, however, as aluminum beryllate.

Identification

It is identified without difficulty by the characteristic form of crystals and aggregates, and by high hardness. Not attacked by acids. Melts with great difficulty (fusibility 7). In fragments distinguishable from beryl by specific gravity and optical properties. In thin sections it is characterized by high relief and by the low value of double refraction.

Origin and Paragenesis

The formation of chrysoberyl is related to pegmatitic and hydrothermal-pneumatolytic processes, and takes place in conditions of general or local enrichment in Al_2O_3 and of the scarcity of SiO_2 in the mineral-forming melts and solutions. A. E. Fersman (1940) discriminates five factors bringing about enrichment in Al_2O_3:

1. primary accumulation of $Al_2O_3 > R_2O + RO$;[1]
2. assimilation of rocks rich in alumina, in which the ratio $Al_2O_3/SiO_2 > \frac{1}{2}$;
3. loss of SiO_2, silica being lost to wall rocks (desilication);
4. decrease of solubility of Al_2O_3 when the composition of the magmatic residue undergoes a change;
5. hydrolysis of previously formed minerals.

In the formation of chrysoberyl the greatest part is played by the second and third factors which manifest themselves in the contact (aluminous) and de-

---

[1] R used for any element of valence indicated. [*Editor.*]

silicated pegmatites and in some contact-metasomatic deposits. The conditions of formation of chrysoberyl determine its usual paragenesis: (1) in ordinary pegmatites with a sign of weak aluminous contamination—garnet, muscovite, feldspars, beryl, quartz, gahnite; (2) in desilicated pegmatites—corundum, spinel, margarite, phlogopite, muscovite, plagioclase, fluorite, apatite; (3) in contact-metasomatic deposits—fluorite, magnetite, vesuvianite, etc. In the hydro-thermal-pneumatolytic deposits aggregates of chrysoberyl are observed in micaceous streaks in metasomatic fluoritic ores.

Deposits of chrysoberyl in pegmatites are numerous, but it does not form large concentrations. The highest concentrations of chrysoberyl are known in the skarns.

Bertrandite, $Be_4[Si_2O_7](OH)_2$

Physical and Optical Properties

Orthorhombic symmetry. Crystal habit of bertrandite is usually tabular. Colorless, white, or yellowish. Glassy luster. Cleavage along (001) perfect, and fair along three directions (100), (010), and (110). Hardness 6. Specific gravity 2.59–2.60. Optically negative, biaxial. 2V = 73° − 75°, N, α = (010); γ = c; γ = 1.611; β = 1.603; α = 1.584; $\gamma - \alpha$ = 0.027.

Chemical Composition

BeO 39.6–42.6 percent; SiO_2 49.3–51.8 percent; H_2O 6.9–8.9 percent.

Identification

Bertrandite is identified outwardly by the characteristic tabular form of orthorhombic crystals. The identification is confirmed by microchemical re-action with quinalizarine and by the checking of optical properties.

Origin and Paragenesis

In pegmatitic veins and in greisens as a late, in some places, a secondary, mineral. In pegmatites, commonly in cavities, it grows on beryl crystals or forms pseudomorphs after them. In greisens and in quartz-wolframite veins it is in irregular accumulations and streaks of small crystals. In some places it is pseudomorphous after the earlier beryllium minerals, beryl and helvite.

Helvite, $Mn_8(BeSiO_4)_6S_2$

Physical and Optical Properties

Cubic symmetry. Crystal form tetrahedral; commonly in irregular rounded forms. Color: red-brown, yellow, yellow-brown, greenish-brown to green. Luster from glassy to pitchy. Cleavage imperfect, resulting in uneven or conchoidal fracture. Hardness 6–6.5. Specific gravity 3.15–3.36; N-1.746.

Chemical Composition

BeO 11–14.2 percent; MnO 28.5–51.6 percent; SiO$_2$ 30.3–35.3 percent; S 5–5.5 percent.

The danalite molecule Fe$_8$(BeSiO$_4$)$_6$S$_2$ usually is present as an isomorphous impurity, therefore, chemical analyses always show iron in addition to manganese. Depending on the content of the danalite molecule one distinguishes helvite and helvite-danalite which is the transitional member of the isomorphous series extending from helvite to danalite. Helvite commonly also contains zinc (the genthelvine species).

Identification

Helvite outwardly resembles garnet in fracture. When in well-developed crystals, it is identified easily by the color and the tetrahedral crystal form. In thin sections it is isotropic, and is characterized by triangular grain boundaries. For the positive identification of small grains one uses the reaction with arsenic or antimony. The powdered mineral or rock presumed to contain helvite is boiled for 1 to 2 minutes in dilute sulphuric acid to which arsenic trioxide has been added. The helvite grains are then coated with a bright yellow film of arsenic trisulphide.

When antimony is used instead of arsenic, the grains of helvite are coated with a bright-red film of antimony trisulphide.

Origin and Paragenesis

Helvite is observed from time to time in albitized pegmatites whose aluminum content has been reduced for some reason. Appreciable accumulations of helvite in such pegmatites are rare and of no commercial importance at present. Larger concentrations of helvite are known in greisens and in wolframite-containing quartz veins; in deposits of these groups helvite is usually accompanied by hematite, fluorite, and some sulfides.

The most representative type of helvite deposit is found in skarns in which helvite usually is present in close paragenesis with magnetite and fluorite; it forms quite sizable accumulations in places.

Danalite, Fe$_8$[BeSiO$_4$]$_6$S$_2$

Physical and Optical Properties

Very similar to helvite. Cubic symmetry. Crystal form octahedral, in which danalite differs from helvite. Commonly occurs as irregular formations and solid masses. Yellow to brown and red. Glassy luster. Hardness 5.5–6. Specific gravity 3.35–3.44. N-1.750–1.759, rather higher than for helvite.

Chemical Composition

One end-member of the isomorphous series, helvite-danalite. Always contains manganese and zinc as impurities. BeO 12.7–14.7 percent; FeO 27–37 percent; SiO_2 29.5–32 percent.

Identification

In crystals it is identified by the form, color, and specific gravity. For positive identification one can use the reaction with arsenic or antimony, as described for helvite.

Origin and Paragenesis

Similar to those for helvite.

CHAPTER 3

Geochemistry of Beryllium[1]

Introduction

Beryllium is one of a group of rare elements of great scientific and practical interest whose geochemistry is still incompletely known. This is largely a result of the difficulty of determining trace amounts of beryllium in minerals and rocks. This difficulty has been overcome relatively recently with the appearance of new accurate methods of chemical and spectrographic analysis (Sandell, 1952).

Beryllium belongs to the second group of Mendeleev's periodic system. Its atomic radius is 1.13Å. The ionic radius of the positive bivalent ion of beryllium is very small, and equals 0.34Å. The ion is highly symmetrical, has the structure of the noble gas type, and is characterized by the lowest polarizability among the ions of this type and by a considerable (second after silicon) polarizing power.

The small radius of the beryllium ion Be^{2+} (the smallest among the metals) strengthens the bond between its valence electrons and the nucleus and is one of the causes of the great stability of the lattices of beryllium minerals. For the same reason, beryllium has a large electronegativity, which approaches that of aluminum. Because of its chemical characteristics (degree of dissociation of its compounds, etc.), beryllium, like aluminum, occupies an intermediate position

[1] This paper, published in Geokhimiya, No. 5, pp. 75–92, 1956, and also presented at the XXth International Geological Congress in Mexico, has been substituted for the original chapter 3 at the request of the author. This has been translated and published previously by the Geochemical Society.

between the typical cations and the complex-forming elements. Covalent bonds play an important role in its oxygen compounds. The amphoteric properties of beryllium are manifested especially strongly in its oxides and halides of the alkali metals, in which beryllium plays the role of a complex-forming element and forms various beryllates.

The co-ordination number of beryllium is 4, and in its natural compounds it is always surrounded by four oxygen ions forming compact $[BeO_4]^{6-}$ tetrahedra.

A remarkable feature of the beryllium-oxygen tetrahedron is its resemblance to the silicon-oxygen tetrahedron $[SiO_4]$, which has nearly the same parameters. There is also a structural resemblance between the beryllium-oxygen and the aluminum-oxygen tetrahedra, although in this case the difference in the parameters is somewhat greater. The similarity of the $[BeO_4]^{6-}$, $[SiO_4]^{4-}$, and $[AlO_4]^{5-}$ tetrahedra plays an exceptionally important role in the geochemistry of beryllium, determining the character of its isomorphism and its double role in the silicate structures.

It is well known (Sobolev, 1952) that the $[SiO_4]$ group occupies an intermediate position between the groups of the $[SO_4]$ and $[PO_4]$ type and the tetrahedral groups of some other oxides, for example MgO_4 in the spinels, which are not distinct from the rest of the structural units of the coordination lattice of a crystal. The tetrahedral groups, $[AlO_4]$ and $[BeO_4]$, have a lower degree of covalent bonding than $[SiO_4]$ and are even more like the common cation-oxygen groups of the crystal lattices. In alkaline media and in compounds with alkali ions, the degree of covalency (and the strength of bonding) within the complex increases and amphoteric tetrahedral groups acquire properties similar to those of the $[SiO_4]$ group; their role in the silicate structures becomes analogous to that of the silicon-oxygen tetrahedron.

Thus, there are beryllium silicates analogous to the alumino-silicates, in which beryllium, substituting for some of the silicon ions, enters into the structure of the complex beryllium-silicon radical. The general composition of this radical may be represented as follows:

$$\{Be_mSi_{n-m}O_{2n}\}^{-2m}, \qquad m \leqslant 0.5n.$$

The radical may be complicated by the replacement of a part of the oxygen ions (in the beryllium-oxygen tetrahedra) by hydroxyl or fluorine:

$$\{Be_mSi_{n-m}O_{2n-l}(OH,F)\}_l^-, \qquad 2m + 1_m \leqslant 0.5n; l \leqslant m.$$

Among the natural beryllium compounds, silicates are predominant. At present 36 beryllium minerals are known of which 63.8 percent are silicates, 16.7 percent phosphates, 8.3 percent oxides, 5.6 percent borates, and 2.8 percent antimonates and carbonates. A list of all beryllium minerals known at present follows:

BERYLLIUM MINERALS

I. OXIDES AND MULTIPLE OXIDES
Bromellite   BeO
Chrysoberyl Al_2BeO_4
Taafeite Al_4MgBeO_8

II. SILICATES
A. TECTOSILICATES

Epididymite $\left.\right\}$ $Na[BeSi_3O_7](OH)$
Eudidymite

Chkalovite $Na_2[BeSi_2O_6]$
Helvite $Mn_8[BeSiO_4]_6S_2$
Danalite $Fe_8[BeSiO_4]_6S_2$
Genthelvite $Zn_8[BeSiO_4]_6S_2$
Bavenite $Ca_4[(Be,Al)_4Si_9(O,OH)_{26}](OH)_2$

Presumed tectosilicates and minerals with undetermined structure

Leucophanite $\left.\right\}$ $Na_{0.6-1}Ca[BeSi_2O_6]$
Meliphanite $Fe_{0.6-1}Ca[BeSi_2O_6]$
Aminoffite $Ca_2[BeSi_2O_6](OH)_2$
Trimerite $(Mn_2,Ca)[BeSiO_4]_3$
Gadolinite $(Y,Ca)_2Fe[BeSiO_4]_2(O,OH)_2$

B. METASILICATES AND DIMETASILICATES
   WITH RING STRUCTURE

Beryl $Al_2Be_3[Si_6O_{18}]$
Milarite $KCa_2(Be_2,Al)[Si_{12}O_{30}]$

C. ORTHOSILICATES WITH NESOSILICATE
   STRUCTURE

Phenacite $\left\{\begin{array}{l}\text{Without additional anions}\\ Be_2[SiO_4]\end{array}\right.$

Euclase $\left\{\begin{array}{l}\text{With OH}^-\\ AlBe[SiO_4](OH)\end{array}\right.$

D. DIORTHOSILICATES WITH NESOSILICATE
   STRUCTURE

Barylite $\left\{\begin{array}{l}\text{Without additional anions}\\ BaBe_2[Si_2O_7]\end{array}\right.$

Bertrandite $\left\{\begin{array}{l}\text{With OH}^-\\ Be_4[Si_2O_7](OH)_2\end{array}\right.$

Gelbertrandite $Be_4[Si_2O_7](OH)_2 \cdot nH_2O$
Spherobertrandite $Be_5[Si_2O_7](OH)_4$
Beryllite $Be_5[Si_2O_7](OH)_4 \cdot 2H_2O$

E. BERYLLIUM ALUMINOSILICATES WITH
   PHYLLOSILICATE STRUCTURE

Beryllium margarite-bityite-bowleyite
   group $(Ca,Na)(Al,Li,Mg)_{2-3}$
   $[(Be,Al)_2Si_2(O,OH,F)_{10}](OH)_4$

III. BORATES
Hambergite $Be_2[BO_3](OH)$
Rhodizite $(K,Na)_{1-2}(Li,Al)_{1.5-4}$
             $Al_4[(Be,B)_3B_4O_{12}]_2(O,OH)_4$

IV. ANTIMONATES
Swedenborgite $NaBe_4SbO_7$

V. PHOSPHATES
Beryllonite $NaBe[PO_4]$
Hurlbutite $CaBe_2[PO_4]$
Herderite $CaBe[PO_4](OH,F)$
Väyrynenite $MnBe[PO_4](OH)$
Moraesite $Be_2[PO_4](OH) \cdot 4H_2O$
Kolveckite $Ca_{0.1}(Al,Be)[(P,Si)O_4] \cdot 2H_2O$

VI. CARBONATES
Beryllium tengerite
   $(Y,Ce)Be[CO_3](OH)_3 \cdot H_2O$

In the geochemical process within the earth's crust, beryllium behaves like a typical lithophile element. This is indicated first of all by its distribution in the different rocks of the lithosphere, although until recently this information has been based on unsystematic investigations of a small number of samples from different regions (Goldschmidt and Peters, 1938; Sandell, 1952) and on the absence of natural beryllium sulfides.

To refine the data on beryllium content in the rocks of the USSR and to determine the laws of its distribution, chemical (analyst S. N. Fedorchuk) and spectrographic (analyst L. I. Sazhina) analyses of over 500 specimens of rocks and minerals from different intrusives in various regions of the Soviet Union were made in the Laboratory of Mineralogy and Geochemistry of Rare Elements between 1953 and 1955. The results of these analyses are presented in Table 7.

The slight discrepancy in the average content of beryllium in the acid, and especially in the alkalic rocks, as compared with the data of Goldschmidt and Peters (1938) and Sandell (1952) (Table 8) may be partly caused by the type of provinces in the USSR and partly by the small number of analyses available to these investigators.

To determine the average beryllium content in the rocks of the USSR,

| **Table 7** | *Beryllium content in the rocks of the USSR* |

ROCKS	NUMBER OF SAMPLES	LOCALITY	RANGE OF CONTENT, %	AVERAGE CONTENT, %
Dunites, pyroxenites	15	Ural Mts., Karelia.	<0.00002	<0.00002
Labradoritites, gabbronorites	9	Ukrainian SSR, Urals.	<0.00002	<0.00002
Gabbros	10 (mixed)	Different regions.	<0.00002	0.00003
Pegmatoidal gabbros	2 (mixed)	Urals.	<0.00002	0.00016
Basalts	10	Different regions.	<0.00005–0.00025	0.00003
Diorites and gabbrodiorites	10	Same.	0.0001–0.0003	0.00018
Biotite granites (Fig. 2)	130	Same.	0.0002–0.0013	0.0004
Two-mica and muscovite granites (Fig. 2)	40	Same.	0.0002–0.0017	0.0009
Average for USSR granites	200	Same.	0.0002–0.0032	0.0005
Acid extrusives	20	Same.	0.0003–0.0020	0.0006
Syenites	10	Same.	0.0003–0.0014	0.0007
Nepheline syenites	5	Mariupol massif.	0.0004–0.0008	0.0006
Nepheline syenites	2 (mixed)	Botogolskii massif.	—	0.0002
Miaskites	4	Ilmen massif.	0.0003–0.0010	0.0007
Miaskites	4	Vishnevogorskii massif.	0.0002–0.0005	0.0004
Nepheline syenites and their varieties (average samples from different complexes)	6[1]	Khibina.	0.0005–0.0008	0.0006
Same	20[2]	Lovozero.	0.0004–0.0024	0.0012

[1] L. S. Borodin's material.
[2] E. M. Eskova's material.

Table 8 | *Average beryllium content in different igneous rocks in percent*

TYPE OF ROCK	AFTER GOLDSCHMIDT, 1932	AFTER SANDELL, 1952	AFTER A. A. BEUS, 1955
Ultrabasic rocks	0	<0.00002	<0.00002
Basic rocks	<0.00036	<0.0001	0.00004
Intermediate (diorites) rocks	—	0.00016	0.00018
Acid rocks	0.00036	0.0003	0.0005
Alkalic rocks	0.0036	—	0.0007[1]

[1] Average for six alkalic massifs of USSR.

a large number of average composite samples systematically collected in different intrusive massifs was analyzed. The average beryllium content (clarke) was then computed on the basis of these data, the relative abundance of the different rocks themselves being taken into consideration (Solov'ev, 1952).

The clarke of beryllium computed for such a large part of the globe as the territory of the USSR probably may be considered as the actual average value of beryllium content in the upper, sialic, part of the lithosphere (Table 9).

Table 9 | *Clarke of beryllium for the upper part of the lithosphere*

CLARKE AND WASHINGTON, 1924[1]	V. M. GOLDSCHMIDT, 1932	A. E. FERSMAN, 1933–1939[1]	A. P. VINOGRADOV, 1949	E. B. SANDELL, 1952	A. A. BEUS, 1955
0.001	0.00017	0.0004	0.0006	0.0002	0.00035
$1 \cdot 10^{-3}$	$1.7 \cdot 10^{-4}$	$4 \cdot 10^{-4}$	$6 \cdot 10^{-4}$	$2 \cdot 10^{-4}$	$3.5 \cdot 10^{-4}$

[1] Hydrosphere included.

Data listed in the tables show that beryllium does not accumulate either in basic or ultrabasic magmas, and usually is present in them in amounts many times smaller than its clarke for the earth's crust as a whole. A certain enrichment in beryllium, very slightly exceeding its clarke, is found in granites, especially in their late muscovite-bearing facies that are more or less affected by the process of autometamorphism, and in alkalic rocks.

Turning now to the question of distribution of beryllium among the minerals of granites, it must be noted that the greater part of it is fixed in the feldspars, which constitute the main mass of these rocks. The highest beryllium concentrations, however, are characteristic of the dark minerals of granites and of muscovite, as is clearly shown in Table 10.

Table 10 | *Distribution of beryllium in the minerals of granites*

ROCK AND ITS MINERALS	LOCALITY	BE CONTENT, %	ROCK AND ITS MINERALS	LOCALITY	BE CONTENT, %
Coarse-grained biotite granite	Eastern Trans-baikalia.	0.0002	Muscovite granite	Urals.	0.0014
Plagioclase from the above granite	Same.	0.0005	Feldspar from the above granite (mainly plagio-clase)	Same.	0.0010
Microcline from the same granite	Same.	0.0001			
Quartz from the same granite	Same.	<0.00002	Quartz from the same granite	Same.	0.00002
Biotite from the same granite	Same.	0.0010	Muscovite from the same granite	Same.	0.0050
Porphyritic biotite granite	Central Trans-baikalia.	0.0008	Average of 10 samples of biotite, two-mica and muscovite granites	Transbai-kalia, Ukraine.	0.0004
Feldspar from the above granite	Same.	0.0007	Quartz	Same.	0.00002
Quartz from the same granite	Same.	0.00002	Feldspars	Same.	0.00035
Dark minerals from the same granite (biotite, hornblende)	Same.	0.0032	Muscovite, biotite, hornblende	Same.	0.0016

The author's data on the distribution of beryllium in the minerals of granites agree with Sandell's (1952) analyses of two samples of acid rocks from the U.S.A.

Whereas in granites the bulk of dispersed beryllium occurs in feldspars, in alkalic rocks it is found mainly in nepheline and feldspars containing 0.0004 to 0.0010 percent Be. In several places the highest beryllium concentrations in the minerals of alkalic rocks have been observed in the varietal dark minerals (aegirine, <0.0025 percent Be; arfvedsonite, <0.0030 percent Be) and especially in some rare earth minerals (eudialyte, <0.010 percent Be, etc.).

The characteristics of behavior of beryllium during the magmatic stage of formation of acid and alkalic rocks are explained by the manner of its diadochic entry into the crystal structures of various silicates.[2] The main factor determining the diadochic substitution of beryllium in silicates is the resemblance between the $[BeO_4]^{6-}$, $[SiO_4]^{4-}$, and $[AlO_4]^{5-}$ groups. A very interesting crystallochemical characteristic of beryllium is the structural resemblance between the polymorphs of beryllium fluoride and the different modifications of silica (Beus, 1956c; Brandenberger, 1932; Hill, 1934). At present three polymorphs of BeF_2 are known, two of which (α-BeF_2 and γ-BeF_2) are structural analogues of cristobalite, and the third, obtained by crystallization of BeF_2 in the presence of NaF between 425° and 528°C, exhibits a clear structural resemblance to α-quartz.

Considering that beryllium and silicon have the same co-ordination number with respect to oxygen, the close resemblance between their ionic radii, the electronegativity of Be^{2+} and Si^{4+}, and also the close similarity of the parameters of the $[BeO_4]^{6-}$, $[BeF_4]^{2-}$, and $[SiO_4]^{4-}$ groups, it is not difficult to explain the substitution of the silicon-oxygen tetrahedra in silicate structures by the beryllium-oxygen, beryllium-fluorine, or beryllium-hydroxyl groups.

At the same time, the existence of numerous beryllium minerals, some of which are quite abundant and occasionally form large economic deposits, suggests that the heterovalent diadochy between beryllium and silicon occurs only under definite, rather strictly limited conditions determined by the physicochemical peculiarities in the process of mineral formation. If this were not so, we would expect a complete dispersion of beryllium resulting from the capture of Be^{2+} ions by the abundant silicates, a phenomenon which does not actually occur. Obviously, the most important factor preventing the capture of beryllium by the silicates is the difference in the electrostatic charges of beryllium and silicon, which requires that a cation with a high charge enter into the lattice at the moment of substitution of $[BeO_4]^{6-}$ for $[SiO_4]^{4-}$ in order to preserve its electrostatic equilibrium.

Thus, the possibility of substitution of $[SiO_4]^{4-}$ by $[BeO_4]^{6-}$ depends in a large measure on the presence or absence during the process of crystallization of free cations with high valence which could restore the equilibrium of the silicate lattice disturbed by the substitution of Be^{2+} for Si^{4+} and compensate for the energy loss involved in such a substitution (Beus, 1953).

Much broader are the possibilities of the silicon-beryllium diadochy accompanied by a substitution of fluorine or hydroxyl for oxygen. It should be con-

---

[2] This question has been discussed in detail in the author's special work (1956c).

sidered, however, that the replacement of the silicon-oxygen tetrahedron in the mineral lattice by a beryllium-fluorine tetrahedron with the electrostatic charge half as high as that of the group being replaced is energetically disadvantageous for the lattice, and this fact must limit the frequency of such substitutions.

In discussing the characteristics of the heterovalent diadochy between beryllium and the cations with similar properties, it must be kept in mind that beryllium may replace not only silicon but also aluminum, which in the aluminosilicates substitutes for the 4-coordinated silicon and forms tetrahedra whose parameters are very near those of the $[SiO_4]$ group.

As a result of a detailed analysis of the data on the traces of beryllium in different minerals, it is possible now to outline its diadochic behavior (Table 11).

Table 11 | *Outline of diadochic behavior of beryllium*

I. Heterovalent diadochic substitutions between silicon and beryllium in the presence of high valence cations

  1. $(K,Na)^+ + [SiO_4]^{4-} \longleftarrow$ (rare earths)$^{3+}$ + $[BeO_4]^{6-}$ ⎤ feldspars, nepheline, garnet,
  2. $2Ca^{2+} + [SiO_4]^{4-} \longleftarrow$ (rare earths)$^{3+}$ + $[BeO_4]^{6-}$ ⎦ aegirine
  3. $2Sc^{3+} + [SiO_4]^{4-} \longleftarrow 2Zr^{4+} + [BeO_4]^{6-}$ thortveitite
  4. $Mg^{2+} + [SiO_4]^{4-} \longleftarrow Ti^{4+} + [BeO_4]^{6-}$ clinohumite, pyroxenes, amphiboles

II. Heterovalent diadochic substitutions between silicon and beryllium in the presence of fluorine and the hydroxyl

  $[SiO_4]^{4-} \longleftarrow [BeO_2(F,OH)_2]^{4-}$ vesuvianite, micas

III. Heterovalent diadochic substitutions between aluminum and beryllium in the presence of the hydroxyl

  $[AlO_4]^{5-} \longleftrightarrow [BeO_3(OH)]^{5-}$ bavenite, bowleyite, bityite, margarite, muscovite, etc.

IV. Isostructural and isomorphous pairs of beryllium compounds

  1. $Be_2[SiO_4]$—$Zn_2[SiO_4]$ phenacite—willemite
  2. $Be_4[Si_2O_7][OH]$—$Zn_4[Si_2O_7][OH]_2 \cdot H_2O$ bertrandite—hemimorphite (possible isomorphism)
  3. $Al_2Be_3[Si_6O_{18}]$—$(Mg,Fe)_2Al_3[Si_5AlO_{18}]$ beryl—cordierite
  4. Al_2BeO_4—$Mg_2[SiO_4]$ chrysoberyl—olivine
  5. Y_2Fe^2–$Be_2Si_2O_{10}$—$Ca_2FeB_2Si_2O_{10}$ gadolinite—homilite
  6. $CaBe(F,OH)_4$—$ZrSiO_4$—$ThSiO_4$ cyrtolite,—thorite (orangite)
  7. $NaLiBe_2(F,OH)_6$—$CaMg[SiO_6]$ diopside (possible)
  8. $CaBe[PO_4][OH,F]$—$CaB[SiO_4][OH]$ herderite—datolite (possible)

The diadochic replacement of silicon by beryllium with the compensation of the electrostatic charge by the simultaneous substitution of a univalent or bivalent cation by the rare earth elements is rather common, although energetically this substitution is disadvantageous (Beus, 1953). In the overwhelming majority of cases, however, the replacement of ions in the silicates by the rare earths and beryllium is very limited and amounts to ten thousandths, thousandths and, rarely, hundredths of one percent. Only in a very small group of rare earth minerals, whose complexity of composition makes possible a whole series of compensating replacements of both cations and anions (allanite, steenstrupine, etc.), is a considerable beryllium content found which occasionally exceeds fractions of one percent.

The diadochic substitution between beryllium and silicon with the simultaneous entry into the lattice of a quadrivalent cation may be illustrated by beryllium-titanclinohumite and thortveitite (Beus 1953, 1956c).

Judging by the available analytical data, the heterovalent substitution of silicon by beryllium with the simultaneous substitution of oxygen by fluorine or the hydroxyl is widespread but limited, as a rule, to tenths of one percent for each of the two replacing ions. The best example of this type of replacement is found in the mica and vesuvianite groups, some of whose members have abnormally high beryllium content exceeding one percent.

The heterovalent substitution of beryllium for the tetrahedrally coordinated aluminum may be exemplified by bavenite, bowleyite, and bityite. Although such examples are rare, the range of the diadochic replacement of aluminum by beryllium in these minerals is considerable and is clearly reflected in their composition.

A very interesting mode of entry of beryllium into minerals is the isostructural isomorphism between beryllium minerals and some zinc, zirconium, and thorium minerals. The similarity of the crystal structure between a certain beryllium and zinc silicate resulting from the crystallochemical similarity of these two elements (ionization potential, activation energy, electronegativity) suggests that under suitable conditions isomorphism may occur between analogous beryllium and zinc minerals. Actually, in those rare cases when these two geochemically distinct elements meet during the process of mineral formation, beryllium is captured by zinc silicates, as, for example, in the case of beryllium-bearing willemite in the unusual contact deposits at Franklin Furnace, N.J., U.S.A.

The significance of the structural similarity between the alkalic and alkaline earth fluoroberyllates and hydroxiberyllates and some silicates cannot be neglected. This structural similarity explains the ever present admixture of one to ten percent of beryllium oxide in the pegmatitic cyrtolite, malacon, and thorite (orangite) (Beus, 1956c).

The crystal structures of the most abundant beryllium mineral, beryl, and of cordierite are also very similar. It is natural to expect, therefore, that under suitable geochemical conditions beryllium may enter the cordierite lattice without disturbing its structure in the least.

This is confirmed by the beryllium-bearing cordierites from a number of pegmatites.

Beryllium in the Magmatic Process

In considering the normal course of crystallization of granitic melts in the light of the above data, it is necessary to note a very important fact which affects the history of beryllium dispersed through the granitic magma. During the early stages of crystallization of granite, the titanium and rare earths contained in the melt become bound in ilmenite and monazite. The negligible beryllium content in the granitic melt precludes the possibility of formation of beryllium minerals during the magmatic stage and the unavailability during the main stages of crystallization of sufficient amounts of free cations with high valence inhibits the capture of beryllium by the lattices of the essential minerals of granite.

The limited dispersion of beryllium in the early minerals crystallizing from granitic magma caused its concentration in the products of the final stages of crystallization, in pegmatites, and in pneumatolytic rocks. The increased beryllium content in the muscovite-bearing fractions of granitic magma subjected in a greater or less degree to the process of autopneumatolysis with the participation of OH and F is very characteristic (Fig. 2). In this case the collector of beryllium is muscovite, which may contain up to 0.005 percent Be (usually 0.001–0.003 percent). It is impossible not to relate this fact with the common association of extensive beryl pegmatite fields with intrusions of biotite granites characterized by a limited development of the muscovite-bearing facies.

Turning now to the distinctive features of crystallization of alkalic magmas, we shall note the following factors which determine the fate of beryllium during the formation of alkalic rocks: (1) the high content of titanium, zirconium, rare earths, and niobium; (2) the prolonged participation of cations with high valences in the process of mineral formation; (3) the alkaline character of the medium which makes the presence of the $[BeO_4]^{6-}$ complex possible. These factors favor the capture of beryllium by the lattices of the rock forming minerals, especially the dark ones, and prevent concentrations of beryllium in alkalic rocks. Although the clarke of beryllium in alkalic rocks is one and a half times as high as in granites, they do not contain marked concentrations of beryllium. At the same time, a number of minerals in these rocks have a relatively high content of diadochic beryllium.

In spite of the relatively high beryllium content in the alkalic rocks as compared with its clarke for the lithosphere, its most characteristic form of occur-

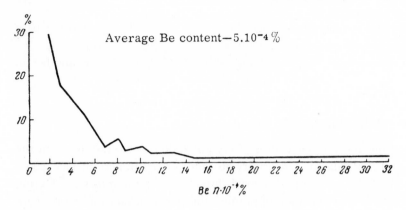

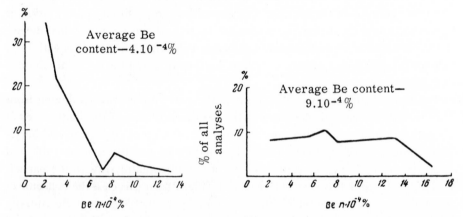

Fig. 2. Distribution of beryllium in granites. Top, beryllium content in granites (based on 200 analyses of average samples and samples from different massifs of the USSR; average Be content is $5 \cdot 10^{-4}\%$). Left, beryllium content in biotite granites (based on the data of 130 analyses of average samples and samples from different massifs of the USSR; average Be content is $4 \cdot 10^{-4}\%$). Right, average beryllium content in two-mica and muscovite granites (based on the data of 40 analyses of average samples and samples from different massifs of the USSR and the Chinese People's Republic; average Be content is $9 \cdot 10^{-4}\%$).

rence in these rocks is in the dispersed state. Concentration of beryllium and formation of beryllium minerals in this case may occur during the postmagmatic reworking of the alkalic rocks resulting in secondary segregation of beryllium.

Beryllium in the Pegmatitic Process

During the pegmatitic process, the granitic magma usually becomes enriched in beryllium[3] in the later stages of the formation of pegmatites when beryllium

[3] Obviously, considerable enrichment may take place when the melt has a relatively high Be content and the factors favoring its dispersion in granites or passage into the pneumatolytic phase are absent.

has an opportunity of building its own lattices with silicon and aluminum and forming a series of beryllium minerals. As a rule, no enrichment in beryllium is found in the early paragenetic associations (zones) of pegmatites and frequently these zones have even lower Be content than the parent granites (Table 12).

Table 12	*Beryllium content in some granites and in the early zones of the related pegmatites*

Be CONTENT IN GRANITES, %	Be CONTENT IN THE GRAPHIC GRANITE ZONE, %	Be CONTENT IN THE BLOCKY MICROCLINE PERTHITE ZONE, %	LOCALITY
0.0002	<0.00005	0.0001	Ukraine
0.0004	0.0003	0.0004	Altai[1]
0.0004	0.0007	0.0002	Transbaikalia[1]
0.0005	0.0003	0.0002	Transbaikalia[1]
0.0007	0.0004	0.0005	Altai[1]

[1] Beryl-bearing pegmatites.

Thus, during the formation of the early zones of primary crystallization (Beus, 1951) only very small amounts of beryllium are removed from the melt and its concentration in the remaining pegmatitic melt or solution increases. Finally, at a certain moment, usually at the end of crystallization of mono-mineralic blocks of microcline-perthite under the conditions of strong oversaturation with silica and accumulation of volatiles (mainly OH), the crystallization of beryl, the main beryllium mineral of the normal granitic pegmatites, begins and continues throughout the pneumatolytic-hydrothermal stage of replacement, until the separation of the last replacing solutions which produce lepidolite and greisen. During this stage in the formation of pegmatite, the characteristics of the migration of beryllium are probably determined by two geochemical factors: (1) the continuously increasing concentration of the volatiles (OH, F, Cl, CO_2) occurring in a virtually closed system, and (2) the high concentration of the alkalies (mainly sodium). It is very probable that under these conditions the highly mobile complex compounds as chlorine, fluorine, and carbonate beryllates of the alkalies form and, as the pegmatite crystallizes, migrate in gaseous form, and later as aqueous solutions, into the still uncrystallized central and upper parts of the pegmatite. That these intermediate compounds are present during the formation of pegmatites is convincingly proved by the abundance in the beryls of different generations of primary microscopic inclusions of chlorides and fluorides of the alkali metals and of fluorite and carbonic acid (Beus, 1956d; Cameron, Rowe, Weiss, 1953). This fact, together with the characteristics of beryllium chemistry, suggests that the process of formation of beryl in pegmatites consists of the dissociation of the mobile beryllium compounds and the fixation of beryllium in the solid phase in the form of the difficulty soluble metasilicate of beryllium and aluminum. This process, depending on the type of participating compounds, must be accompanied by a continuous separation and removal of soluble alkali halides or carbonic acid. A very small part of these substances is captured by the growing crystal and forms inclusions which testify convincingly to the important role of the halides and carbonate compounds in the migration of beryllium and formation of beryl.

Each stage of the pegmatitic process corresponds to a definite generation of beryl which reflects in its composition the geochemical features of the given stage (Beus, 1956a; Ginzberg, 1955). The block pegmatite zones are characterized by the formation of bluish-green, green, and yellow beryl with low alkali content. The large, sometimes gigantic, beryl crystals and crystal aggregates of this generation usually grow at the boundary between the quartz core of the pegmatite and the surrounding feldspathic zone. In other places, beautifully developed crystals of alkali-free beryl occur in the blocky quartz of the core at some distance from its boundary with the outer pegmatite zones.

Evidently this generation of beryl is not related to the process of alkali replacement in pegmatites. Very probably the euhedral prismatic crystals of alkali-free beryl form in the process of dissociation of the mobile beryllium compounds under the conditions of relative freedom existing in the central part of the pegmatite before the crystallization of the blocky quartz of the pegmatite core (Beus, 1954). This is indicated in part by the fact that the large prismatic beryl crystals are cut and healed by blocky quartz.

The quartz-muscovite, quartz-albite-muscovite, and albite replacing complexes in the albite-muscovite and spodumene-albite pegmatites[4] are characterized by the presence of light green, greenish-white, and white sodium and sodium-lithium-bearing beryl with a markedly high sodium and lithium content. The numerous facts observed during a detailed study of beryl pegmatites suggest that the sodium and sodium-lithium varieties of beryl form metasomatically by replacement of microcline by beryllium-bearing alkaline solutions separated during the process of crystallization of the late siliceous pegmatitic melt which forms the zone of blocky quartz (Beus, 1954). The liberated alkaline solutions replace parts of the pegmatite surrounding the zone of blocky quartz and produce the characteristic albite and muscovite-albite aureoles around the quartz core. Some of the solution penetrates along fractures into the border regions and, migrating along the weakened contact zones of the pegmatite into its upper parts, forms clearly defined endocontact zones of replacement. The

---

[4] For the basis of paragenetic classification of pegmatites and their zones, see Beus, 1951.

character of the spatial distribution of albitized zones in pegmatites determines also the distribution of sodium and sodium-lithium beryl.

Judging by the paragenetic characteristics of sodium and sodium-lithium beryl, its formation may be represented in the following general way:

$$KAlSi_3O_8 + H_2O + NaOH + NaBe(Cl,F) \longrightarrow$$

Microcline   Alkaline solution containing

beryllium

$$Na[AlSi_3O_8] + KAl_2[AlSi_2O_{10}](OH)_2 + SiO_2 + Al_2Be_3[Si_6O_{18}]$$

Albite   Muscovite   Quartz   Beryl

$\uparrow$

| Removal of alkali halides |
+ H_2O + (K,Na) (Cl,F)
solution

In some cases in the later stages of replacement, recrystallization and partial solution of beryl may occur accompanied by its redeposition in the form of sodium and sodium-lithium beryl characteristic of cleavelandite and lepidolite replacing complexes. This is seen especially clearly if the recrystallization of the earlier generations of beryl has been incomplete (Beus, 1956d). The replacement stages are characterized also by the formation of a series of secondary beryllium minerals including silicates (phenacite, bavenite, euclase) and various phosphates. It should be noted also that during the replacement stages the process of dispersion of beryllium is intensified because of the capture of a part of its ions by the lattices of the rock-forming minerals crystallizing from the replacing pegmatitic solutions. The principal collectors of beryllium are albite and micas (Table 13). It should be mentioned, however, that in beryl pegmatites containing more than 0.1 percent of beryl, the total mass of dispersed beryllium is many times smaller than the mass of beryllium concentrated in the beryl minerals. Computations made for a group of pegmatitic beryl deposits containing 0.1 to 0.5 percent of beryl show that the ratio ($P:K$) of the beryllium dispersed in various minerals (P) to the beryllium concentrated in the form of beryl (K) in these pegmatites varies from 1:2 to 1:20.

In these pegmatites the important geochemical factor favoring concentration of beryllium in beryllium minerals (even if the Be content is low) is its very slight dispersion, due, in part, to the negligible role played by the elements which could compensate for the entry of beryllium into the silicate lattices.

Beryllium behaves somewhat differently in the granites with relatively high content of rare earths, niobium, tantalum, and titanium. Here a considerable amount of beryllium is dispersed by diadochic substitution in feldspars, allanite, cyrtolite, and the metamict yttrium earth tantalate-niobates (fergusonite,

| Table 13 | *Content of dispersed beryllium in minerals and mineral aggregates of simple pegmatites[1]* |

MINERAL OR ROCK	NUMBER OF SAMPLES FROM DIFFERENT REGIONS	PEGMATITES WITHOUT RARE EARTHS (UKRAINE)	PEGMATITES WITH BERYLLIUM MINERALS		PEGMATITES WITH RARE EARTH MINERALS BUT NOT CONTAINING Be MINERALS
			RANGE	AVERAGE	
Graphic granite	14	0.0001–0.0002	0.0003–0.0007	—	0.0001–0.0002
Medium-grained pegmatite with tourmaline and garnet	6	0.0001–0.0003	—	—	—
Blocky microcline perthite	30	0.0001–0.0003	0.0005–0.0036	0.0008	0.0012–0.0020
Blocky oligoclase	3	—	—	—	0.0019–0.0036
Blocky quartz	9	0.0001	0.0004–0.00005	0.0002	0.0001
Albite	30	—	0.0004–0.0061	0.0018	—
Muscovite	30	0.0001	0.0020–0.0108	0.0056	0.0040
Lepidolite	10	—	0.0016–0.0126	0.0050	—
Black tourmaline	4	—	0.0013–0.0036	—	—
Polychromic tourmaline	2	—	0.0020–0.0036		—
Garnet	3	—	0.0006–0.0020	—	—
Spodumene	5	—	0.0005 0.0072	0.0010	—
Apatite	1	—	0.0018	—	—
Cyrtolite	2	—	—	—	0.0056–0.0210
Monazite	1	—	—	—	0.0028
Allanite	4	—	—	—	0.0124–0.685

[1] Analyses by S. N. Fedorchuk.

yttrotantalite, etc.). Relatively high concentrations of beryllium have been found in some minerals (including oligoclase and microcline) of the blocky zones of the Baltic shield pegmatites containing notable amounts of the yttrium earth tantalate-niobates (Table 13). An analysis of the feldspars for the rare earths confirmed the presence of yttrium in oligoclase and of lanthanum in microcline. In spite of the high beryllium content in these pegmatites, beryllium minerals are absent from them. Under favorable conditions (presence of iron and absence of boron) and with high concentrations of beryllium, gadolinite forms in the rare earth pegmatites. Naturally, under these conditions, the formation of beryl is inhibited and deposits containing considerable amounts of gadolinite and beryl or of a rare earth tantalate-niobate and beryl, are very rare.

Returning now to the question of distribution of beryllium in pegmatites, it is necessary to point out that phenacite, chrysoberyl, gadolinite, and other beryllium minerals play an insignificant role in the general balance of beryllium in granite pegmatites, which includes beryllium atoms fixed in beryl and those dispersed through the lattices of the rock-forming minerals of the pegmatites.

The great variation in the beryllium content in the pegmatites of different types and regions makes it difficult to compute the clarke of beryllium in pegmatites. In this computation it is necessary to consider: (1) the difference in the beryllium content in the pegmatites of the rare earth provinces and in the provinces from which the rare earths are absent; (2) the difference in the content of dispersed beryllium and beryllium concentrated in beryllium minerals in different types of pegmatites; (3) the quantitative relations between groups of pegmatites differing in beryllium content and, first of all, between pegmatites with beryllium minerals and those without them.

The results of study of beryllium distribution in pegmatites (Beus, 1955) and the analysis of the available material on the relations of different types of pegmatites in the most typical rare earth pegmatite fields give an average weight clarke of beryllium in pegmatites as 0.0020 percent (Table 14).

Table 14	*Weight clarkes of beryllium in different groups of granitic pegmatites*

GROUPS OF PEGMATITES	RANGE OF BERYLLIUM CONTENT
Pegmatite without rare earth minerals (not albitized)	0.0002–0.0010
Blocky pegmatites with rare earth minerals (without beryl)	0.0010–0.0025
Pegmatites containing 0.01–0.1% beryl	0.0015–0.0057
Pegmatites containing 0.2–0.5% beryl	0.0100–0.0250
Average for all pegmatites	0.0020

The data obtained by the author make it possible to refine the clarke of beryllium in pegmatites (0.05 percent) derived previously by Fersman (1940). His very high clarke may be true only for exceptional pegmatites containing more than 1 percent of beryl.

The geochemical history of beryllium in alkalic pegmatites is still very poorly known, but everything that has been said about the role of beryllium in alkalic rocks is applicable in even greater measure to alkalic pegmatites. The relatively high beryllium, titanium, zirconium, and rare earth content in the alkalic pegmatitic melts creates favorable conditions for the diadochic entry of beryllium into the lattices of many silicates of alkalic pegmatites.

The distinctive features of the agpaitic alkalic process, the predominance of $Na_2O + K_2O$ over Al_2O_3 and the possible presence of beryllium in the form of the $[BeO_4]^{6-}$ groups, determine the character of the relatively rare beryllium minerals found in alkalic pegmatites (epididymite, chkalovite, eudidymite, leucophanite, and meliphanite). The majority of these minerals may be considered as alkalic beryllium silicates. The beryllium minerals of alkalic pegmatites usually appear during the last stages of their formation and are typical late minerals of the soda metasomatism stage. Of especial geochemical interest is the solution of the problem of secondary concentration and redeposition of beryllium during the process of metasomatism of the early minerals of alkalic pegmatites containing diadochic admixtures of beryllium.

Beryllium in the Pneumatolytic and Hydrothermal Processes

The principle of limited migration of beryllium and its concentration exclusively in granite pegmatites enunciated some time ago by V. M. Goldschmidt and supported by a number of investigators (Fersman, 1936–1939; Rankama and Sahama, 1950) must be revised. During the emplacement of beryllium-bearing intrusives under thermodynamic conditions excluding the possibility of formation of pegmatites and also in the presence of extractors-mineralizers such as fluorine, beryllium together with lithium, tungsten, tin, and molybdenum passes into the pneumatolytic products of granitic magma and into hydrothermal veins.

Almost all beryllium minerals characteristic of granitic pegmatites are found in hydrothermal-pneumatolytic rocks related to granitic magma, and some of them are more common in hydrothermal-pneumatolytic deposits than in pegmatites (euclase, bertrandite, and others). The high beryllium concentrations in the form of beryllium minerals in the hydrothermal-pneumatolytic deposits are known in many regions of the globe but have been little studied. Most deposits of this type are characterized by the association of beryllium with fluorine (an intimate association of beryllium minerals with topaz and fluorite), which indicates the rather significant role of beryllium fluorides in the removal of beryllium compounds from the magma.

It should be noted that the paragenesis and composition of beryllium minerals in the hydrothermal-pneumatolytic deposits is determined in most cases by the character of the country rocks subjected to pneumatolytic action (Table 15).

The precipitant of beryllium from gases and solutions in acid and aluminous rocks is aluminum, which is liberated from the rocks and reacts with the components of the mineralizing solutions during the process of greisenization. In the case of carbonate rocks, the passage of beryllium into the solid phase is

	CHARACTERISTIC	CHARACTERISTIC
ENCLOSING ROCKS	BERYLLIUM MINERALS	PARAGENESIS

Table 15 | *Paragenesis of beryllium minerals in hydrothermal-pneumatolytic deposits*

ENCLOSING ROCKS	CHARACTERISTIC BERYLLIUM MINERALS	CHARACTERISTIC PARAGENESIS
Granites and other acid and intermediate igneous and metamorphic rocks.	Beryl, bertrandite, euclase.	Quartz, topaz, micas.
Aluminum rocks.	Beryl, chrysoberyl.	Zinnwaldite, siderophyllite, topaz, to a less extent, fluorite.
Carbonate rocks.	Chrysoberyl, phenacite, helvite-danalite.	Fluorite, lithian margarite.

probably caused by the dissociation of beryllium fluoride as a result of its reaction with calcium carbonate and the fixation of fluorine in fluorite.

In this connection, the assemblage of beryllium minerals characteristic of deposits in carbonate rocks is of considerable interest. The main beryllium minerals of such deposits are phenacite and chrysoberyl, formed as a result of the pneumatolytic-hydrothermal reactions, the replacement of limestones by fluorite, and the formation of skarns at the contacts between granite and limestone, either in an undersilicated (desilication) or aluminum-poor environment, depending on the course of the process. In many vein deposits in limestones there are characteristic accumulations of helvite and danalite, which form when high concentrations of iron and manganese are present during the process of crystallization.

The geochemical history of beryllium in the meso- and epithermal processes is completely unknown. However, the presence of beryllium minerals (euclase, milarite) in the veins of Alpine type, and also the development of helvite during the later stages of formation of certain polymetallic deposits, indicate the extensive migration of beryllium under hydrothermal conditions.

In the existing mineral waters, beryllium is present in a number of places in amounts up to $n \cdot 10^{-6}$ percent. For example, the waters of some of the Transbaikalian carbonate springs contain up to $6 \cdot 10^{-5}$ g/l Be.

Analysis of the available data on the hydrothermal-pneumatolytic deposits of beryllium leads to the conclusion that the formation of high concentrations of beryllium in the hydrothermal-pneumatolytic process coincides in time and space with the formation of pneumatolytic and hypothermal deposits of tungsten, tin, and molybdenum. The degree and scale of beryllium concentration in these deposits are frequently many times as great as in the pegmatites.

Beryllium in the Contact Metasomatic Process

The contact metasomatic rocks resulting from the reaction between beryllium-bearing granites and limestones are characterized, as a rule, by a much higher beryllium content as compared with its clarke for the lithosphere.

The most common beryllium minerals in the contact metasomatic rocks are helvite and danalite, not uncommon are chrysoberyl and phenacite. Mineralogical-chemical analyses of the known skarn deposits with high contents of beryllium minerals reveal the conditions which favor beryllium concentration in the contact metasomatic process. The principal conditions (apart from the necessary relatively high beryllium concentration in the magma) are: (1) a high fluorine content in the magmatic chamber, which insures extraction and removal of beryllium from the magma; (2) a relatively low concentration of silicon during the formation of skarns, which inhibits the formation of silicates; and (3) the absence of certain cations with high valence, which, if present, would favor the dispersion of beryllium in the silicate lattices.

The formation of the helvite-danalite group of minerals occurs in an environment with high concentration of iron and manganese and scarcity of silicon and aluminum at the contacts between beryllium-bearing granites and limestones. The very characteristic associates of the minerals of this group in the contact metasomatic zones are magnetite and fluorite. The dominance of silicates in the skarns usually leads to the dispersion of beryllium and prevents the formation of the helvite group of minerals. As an example, the skarns of Iron Mountain in New Mexico (U.S.A.) (Jahns, 1944) may be cited in which the increase in the proportion of the silicates from 11.2 to 18.5 percent is accompanied by a decrease in the content of helvite-danalite from 11.2 to 0.7 percent, while the content of BeO in the most abundant silicate, vesuvianite, rises to 1 percent. Investigations of helvite occurrences show that the main quantity of beryllium in contact metasomatic deposits is introduced together with fluorine during the concluding stage of the formation of skarn, and accumulates in the form of helvite and danalite in the silicate-poor ores enriched in magnetite. Phenacite and chrysoberyl in the beryllium-bearing skarns are also intimately associated with fluorine, being the products of reaction of fluorine-bearing emanations and hydrothermal solutions with limestone. The formation of phenacite and chrysoberyl during contact metasomatism is favored by desilication of the mineralizing solutions analogous to that mentioned above in connection with pneumatolytic fluorite deposition in limestones.

Beryllium in the Supergene Processes

The routes of migration of beryllium during supergene processes have been studied little. Rankama and Sahama (1950) conclude on the basis of the similarity between the ionic potentials of beryllium ($\Phi Be^{2+} = 5.88$) and aluminum ($\Phi Al^{3+} = 5.26$) that the migration routes of the two elements during the supergene processes are also similar. In this he agrees with Goldschmidt. Fersman (1936–1939), ascribing the decisive role to the high polarization power of beryllium ions, points out the possibility of adsorption of beryllium in the supergene zone on clays and soils.

It should be noted that the existing analytical data on the distribution of beryllium in sedimentary rocks do not confirm its relationship to aluminum. With the concentration of aluminum in bauxites being four to five times as high as its clarke in the lithosphere, the relative concentration of beryllium in the bauxites varies with respect to its clarke, from 0.3 to 6. At the same time, in clays and especially in kaolinites which have a relatively low concentration of aluminum as compared with its clarke (less than 2), the coefficient of enrichment in beryllium as compared with its clarke reaches 60. An especially high beryllium content is found in clays lying near deposits enriched in beryllium to a greater or less degree.

The average beryllium content in a mixture of 53 redeposited clays from different regions of the USSR is 0.0007 percent, which is near the data for clays obtained by Goldschmidt (0.0006 percent) and is twice as high as the clarke of beryllium in the lithosphere.

The role of adsorption in the precipitation of beryllium on colloidal and finely dispersed systems from aqueous solutions may be illustrated by the following example. A sample of mine water at one of the pegmatite deposits of beryl contained $1 \cdot 10^{-5}$ g/l Be. After some time, a colloidal precipitate was deposited from the water which consisted mainly of oxides of iron, manganese, and alumina. An analysis of the filtered sediment revealed 0.03 percent Be. No beryllium was found in the residue left after evaporation of the filtrate.

A. P. Vinogradov's research (36 papers) on the geochemistry of soils also points to the strong affinity of beryllium for clayey soils. It is necessary to point out that in the regions containing deposits of beryllium minerals and rocks with high beryllium content, soils are known to be enriched in this element. It is interesting in this connection to note the role of beryllium in the biogeochemical processes. In discussing the accumulation of rare elements in plants and coals,

Goldschmidt and Peters (1938) noted that they have considerable concentrations of beryllium.

It should be noted that a relatively high beryllium content (up to hundredths of one percent) is found in the ashes of plants growing in the regions of beryllium-bearing pegmatites and certain alkalic rocks. Further investigations of this phenomenon should provide interesting data.

In conclusion, it must be said that investigation of the geochemistry of beryllium began only recently and is quite inadequate to give a complete geochemical history of this most interesting element. The available data suffice only to outline the principal features of the behavior of beryllium in the different geochemical processes. Further development and refinement of this subject is a problem for the near future.

Types of Beryllium Deposits

There is no generally accepted classification of beryllium deposits; that suggested in this publication is one of the possible classifications and is based on the genetic and paragenetic features of beryllium deposits. Also, it should be noted that the present stage of knowledge of beryllium raw materials make it impossible to limit oneself to the description of the beryllium deposits of commercial types only, because a number of types which are at present not exploited industrially, owing to the lack of suitable processes of beneficiation and processing of ores, may acquire in the future a considerable importance as a real commercial source of beryllium.

Pegmatitic Beryllium Deposits

The beryllium-bearing pegmatitic fields are related spatially to the exo-contact and endo-contact zones of medium-depth granite intrusions that occur most frequently in the cores of large anticlinal structures, the limbs or the axial part of which are disrupted to a greater or lesser extent by regional fractures.

The structure of pegmatite fields is usually determined by the peculiarities of the disjunctive tectonics of the roof of the granite intrusion, and by the nature

Table 16　　*Genetic types of beryllium deposits*

TYPES OF DEPOSITS	ENCLOSING ROCKS	BERYLLIUM MINERALS		CHARACTERISTIC PARAGENESIS		EXAMPLES OF FOREIGN DEPOSITS	INDUSTRIAL IMPORTANCE ABROAD
		MAIN	MINOR	MAIN MINERALS	ACCOMPANYING RARE-METAL MINERALS		
				PEGMATITIC DEPOSITS			
Miarolitic, streaky (syngenetic) granite pegmatites.	Granites, gneissic granites.	Beryl.	Phenacite.	Microcline, quartz, albite.	—	Brazil (Minas-Geraes), etc.	Precious stones.
Block and fully differentiated biotite-microcline granite pegmatites.	Granites, gneissic granites, gabbro, amphibolites.	Gadolinite or beryl.	—	Microcline (ordinary or amazonite), quartz, biotite.	Fergusonite and other tantalo-niobates of rare earths; allanite, xenotime, monazite.	U.S.A., Texas (Baringer Hill), South Norway (Iveland, Setersdalen, etc.).	Very rare sub-type; can be used as source of yttrium and rare earths of its group.
Block and fully differentiated muscovite-microcline granite pegmatites.	Granites of the endo-contact part of intrusions; various magmatic and metamorphic rocks of the roof of intrusions.	Beryl.	Phenacite, chrysoberyl, bertrandite, herderite, beryllonite, etc.	Microcline, quartz, muscovite, albite, black tourmaline, iron and manganese phosphates.	Triphylite, columbite-tantalite.	North-east Brazil (Rio Grande do Norte, Paraiba), India (Rajputana, etc.), Argentina, Madagascar, etc.	Widespread sub-type. Commercially important.
Replaced muscovite-albite granite pegmatites.	Do.	1. Beryl (sodium and sodium-lithium variety).	Bertrandite, beryllonite, herderite, etc.	Albite, quartz, muscovite, spessartite.	Lithiophilite, tourmaline, columbite-tantalite.	Australia (Wodgina), China, U.S.A. (Conn. etc.), north-east Brazil, etc.	Do.
		2. Helvite.	Phenacite.	Albite, quartz.	Columbite-tantalite.		Rare type.
Replaced spodumene-albite and lepidolite-albite granite pegmatites.	Do.	Beryl (rosterite and vorobyevite).	Beryllonite, bertrandite, phenacite, etc.	Albite, quartz, muscovite, polychromic tourmalines, spessartite.	Lithiophilite, amblygonite, columbite-tantalite, microlite, spodumene, pollucite, lepidolite, petalite.	U.S.A. (New Mexico—Harding deposit—etc.), South-West Africa.	Important commercial type, exploited for the rare elements.

Granite pegmatites of the crossing line (mica-plagioclase veins).	Ultra-basic rocks, serpentinites.	Beryl.	Emerald, phenacite, chrysoberyl, bavenite.	Oligoclase, albite, phlogopite, quartz, margarite.	—	Africa (Transvaal—Somerset mine deposit—etc.), Australia (Poona etc.).	Fairly rare valuable commercial type.
Replaced hackmanite-natrolite, albite-natrolite and ussingite pegmatites of nepheline syenites.	Poikilitic nepheline syenites, lujavrites.	Epididymite.	Euddidymite, chkalovite.	Albite, natrolite, hackmanite, aegirine or eudialyte, ussingite.	—	Greenland.	No commercial value.
HYDROTHERMAL-PNEUMATOLYTIC DEPOSITS							
Quartz-muscovite, quartz-topaz, quartz-beryl greisens.	Granite.	Beryl, helvite.	Bertrandite, phenacite, bavenite.	Quartz, muscovite, topaz, fluorite.	Cassiterite, wolframite.	U.S.A. (Nevada, South Dakota).	Are studied in connection with work on the development of methods for the beneficiation of disseminated beryl.
Feldspar-quartz, quartz, mica-quartz, and other veins.	Granites and granite-enclosing metamorphic rocks.	Beryl.	Bertrandite, phenacite, helvite.	Quartz, fluorite, muscovite.	Wolframite, cassiterite, molybdenite.	U.S.A. (New Mexico, Luna Co; Colorado, Chaffee Co., etc.); Argentina (San Louis province), etc.	Are studied in connection with work on the development of methods for the beneficiation of disseminated beryl.
Quartz, quartz-hematite veins.	Granites, limestones.	Helvite, danalite.	Beryl, bertrandite, phenacite.	Quartz, muscovite, hematite, sulfides.	Wolframite, cassiterite, molybdenite.		None as yet.
Fluorite pneumatolytes and hydrothermalites in limestones.	Limestones.	Phenacite, chrysoberyl.	Euclase.	Fluorite, muscovite.	Cassiterite.	U.S.A. (Alaska, Seward peninsula, Cape Mountain and Lost River deposits).	None as yet.
Skarns (fluorite-mica-magnetite).	Do.	Helvite, danalite, chrysoberyl.	Phenacite, beryl.	Fluorite, vesuvianite, magnetite, mica.		U.S.A. (New Mexico, Iron Mountain and other deposits).	Are studied in connection with the development of the technological flowsheet.
HYDROTHERMAL DEPOSITS							
Carbonate veins.	Limestones.	Beryl (emerald), helvite.	—	Calcite.	Parisite.	Columbia (Muso district).	No information.
Alpine veins.	Metamorphozed rocks.	Euclase.	Phenacite, milarite, bavenite.	Quartz, orthoclase, zeolites.	—	Switzerland, Germany.	None.

of relief of its apical part. The part played by these factors varies according to the depth of erosion of the granite intrusion.

The elements of the disjunctive tectonics of the roof are the determining factors of the structure of pegmatitic fields which are connected with granite intrusions partly exposed by erosion. In this case the pegmatitic field is usually controlled by a major fracture zone and extends for tens of kilometers parallel to the disrupted zone (Fig. 3).

The part played by the regional disjunctive structures is much less pronounced in the beryl-bearing fields connected with intrusions whose apical part is to a large extent removed by erosion. In this case the relief of the apex of the intrusion becomes the factor determining the structure of the pegmatitic field. The pegmatitic formations of the group in question are concentrated in those portions of the depressions on the apex of the intrusion that contain the remains of the roof-rocks; they also form accumulations within the exo-contact or endo-contact zones of the granite mass (Fig. 4).

Characteristic of all pegmatite areas is the non-uniform distribution of pegmatites within a large pegmatitic field. Parts containing abundant pegmatites alternate with parts almost completely devoid of them; in this connection there are isolated smaller pegmatitic fields of the second order or individual pegmatitic

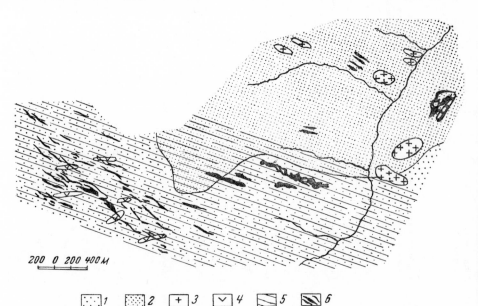

200 0 200 400 M

Fig. 3. Pegmatitic field controlled by the zone of fracture at the limb of the anticlinal fold (slight degree of erosional exposure of the granite intrusion). (1) Sandstone-shale series; (2) sandstone-conglomerate series; (3) cupolae of two-mica granites; (4) dikes of basic rocks; (5) zone of rupture; (6) pegmatite dikes.

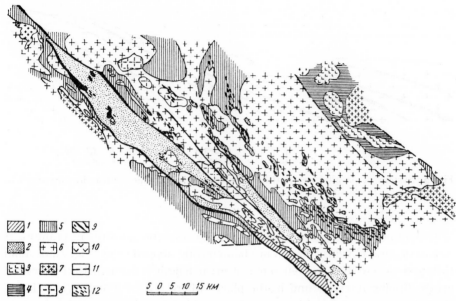

Fig. 4. Pegmatitic field related to the roof remnants preserved in depressions of the apical part of the granite intrusion. (1) Tuffs and shales of the Upper Devonian; (2) sandstones and shales of the Middle Devonian; (3) porphyrys and tuffs of the Middle Devonian; (4) shales and sandstones of the Lower Silurian; (5) schists of preCambrian (?); (6) gneissic granites; (7) massive granites; (8) porphyritic granites; (9) fracture intrusions of granites and aplites in rupture zones; (10) diorites and gabbro; (11) ruptures; (12) pegmatites.

deposits. The structure of these deposits is determined in each particular case by the specific geological conditions of the particular area. In the case of pegmatitic formations that transgress the enclosing rocks, the main factor controlling the structure of the deposit is the nature of the fractures utilized by the ore-bearing melt-solution. In the case of "inter-bed" conformable pegmatites the main factors controlling the structure of the ore body are the elements and the nature of occurrence of the enclosing schistose rocks.

Morphological Features of Beryl-bearing Pegmatites

The morphological features of the beryl-bearing pegmatitic formations are diverse and are determined, in the first place, by the nature of the enclosing rocks.

In the massive competent rocks (granites, gabbros, amphibolites, etc.) the most common form of pegmatites is the vein; less common are stock-shaped bodies and still rarer are pipes.

One can outline the following most characteristic groups of beryl-bearing pegmatites occurring in the fissures of massive rocks:

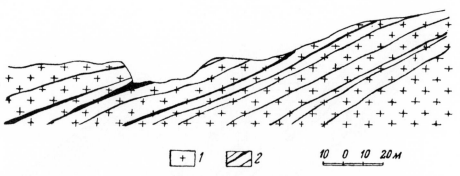

Fig. 5. System of parallel pegmatitic veins in gently-dipping contraction fractures in granites. (1) Granite; (2) pegmatite veins.

1. The pegmatites occupy the system of contraction fissures in granites. A system of parallel veins (Fig. 5), or characteristic stepped veins (Fig. 7), of small thickness (a few meters), but often of great length is formed. In the crests of gently-dipping fractures and in the places where several fractures join dome-shaped bulges are formed in many places, which contain increased concentrations of rare-metal minerals, including beryl (Fig. 6).

2. The pegmatites occupy the system of shear fractures in igneous rocks. A series of adjacent, parallel, en echelon veins results, whose length is measured in hundreds of meters, while the thickness ranges from fractions of one meter to 4 to 5 m. Dikes as much as 1000 m long and as much as 10 m or more wide, are formed in the zones of large ruptures (Fig. 8).

3. The pegmatitic melt-solution utilizes the areas where two systems of fractures, steeply dipping and gently dipping, intersect. In this case, stepped veins most frequently form with alternate areas of gentle and steep dip (Fig. 9). When individual blocks are displaced relative to one another, stock-shaped

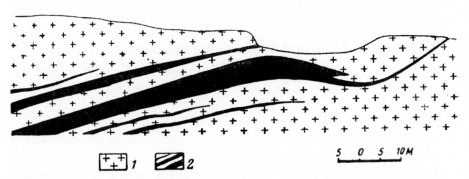

Fig. 6. Beryl-bearing dome-shaped bulge in the crest section of a gently-dipping pegmatite vein. (1) Granite; (2) pegmatite veins.

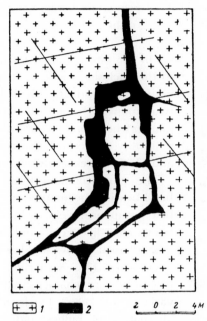

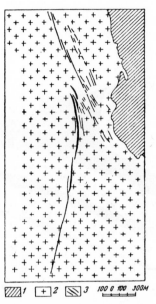

Fig. 7. Stepped pegmatite vein in the contraction fractures of granites. (1) Granite; (2) pegmatite.

Fig. 8. Pegmatite dikes in shear fractures in massive rocks. (1) Schists of the endo-contact zone; (2) granites; (3) pegmatitic dikes.

bulges can form, whose dimensions in cross section in many places are measured in hundreds of meters (Figs. 10 and 11). Bodies of this kind are usually of considerable commercial interest.

4. In the fractures of small plutons of ultra-basic or basic rocks occurring among gneisses or crystalline schists, in many places there are isolated, quite wide plate-shaped or loaf-shaped pegmatites that sharply thicken on passing from the basic pluton into the enclosing rocks.

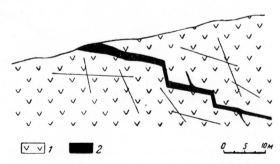

Fig. 9. Stepped pegmatite vein formed at the intersection of two systems of fractures. (1) Gabbro; (2) pegmatite.

Somewhat different forms are characteristic of pegmatitic bodies occurring in plastic rocks, mainly in various schists which are the most common rocks in the roofs of pegmatite-bearing intrusions.

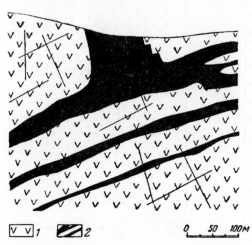

On the basis of their relation to the enclosing rocks, such pegmatites are distinctly divided in two groups: (1) concordant pegmatites whose contacts parallel the schistosity of the enclosing rocks; and (2) transgressive pegmatites.

The most common forms of beryl-bearing pegmatites of the first group are: vein, vein with bulges, lens-like vein, and lens. Stock-shaped bodies are less frequent (Fig. 12). As a rule, the pegmatites are characterized by variable thickness, by frequent alternation of bulges and contractions and, except in rare cases, by relatively small dimensions.

Fig. 10. Thick stock-like bulge of the pegmatite formed as a result of displacement of blocks in the area of intersection of two systems of fractures. (1) Gabbro; (2) pegmatite veins.

The morphological features of pegmatites of this group are responsible for the complexity of the exploration and evaluation of beryl deposits.

The most common form of transgressive pegmatites is the dike. As a rule, dikes fill up shear-fractures in the zones of large ruptures; they are found to extend as much as 1 km and more in length, the thickness being 5–15 m (see Fig. 3). By drilling, individual dikes have been detected to extend for several hundreds of meters along the dip without any appreciable change of thickness.

When useful minerals are present in it, this morphological type of pegmatite is promising from the economic aspect.

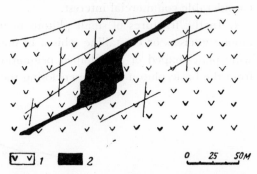

Fig. 11. Thick stock-like bulge of the pegmatite formed as a result of displacement of blocks in the area of intersection of two systems of fractures. (1) Gabbro; (2) pegmatite.

Less characteristic are the transgressive vein-like bodies of small thickness, usually associated with small fault-fissures. In many places this vein type is characterized by an extremely irregular form. An irregular capricious form with branches and apophyses is common in the mixed type of veins which utilize bedding planes and transgress the schistosity of the enclosing rocks.

Concluding the description of the morphological features of the granite pegmatites, one should note that the form most typical of pegmatites is not characteristic of the common magmatic and hydrothermal-pneumatolytic deposits. To the latter belong veins with very thick bulges, thick and relatively short lenses, and irregular bodies that are formed both in the igneous and schistose rocks. The morphological features of these bodies point to their having been formed in conditions of a very great internal pressure.

At the same time pegmatites show a number of forms which are characteristic, on the one hand, of vein-like magmatic rocks (dikes, veins) and, on the other hand, of the hydrothermal-pneumatolytic deposits (veins, ladder veins, pipes).

Paragenetic Peculiarities of the Pegmatitic Beryllium Deposits

The discrimination of separate genetic groups of the pegmatitic beryllium deposits is based on the texture-paragenetic classification of the granite pegmatites, advanced by K. A. Vlasov (1952), and on the paragenetic-zonal classification of the granite pegmatites, suggested by the author in 1951 (Table 17).

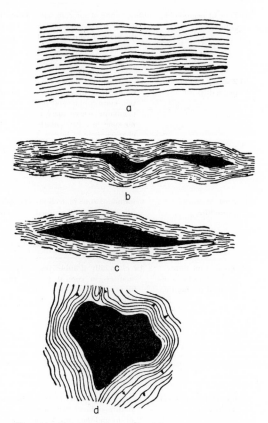

Fig. 12. Forms of interbedded pegmatites in schistose rocks. (a) vein; (b) vein with bulges; (c) lens; (d) stock.

In the geological exploration and prospection for rare metals both classifications have withstood the test of time, and are used by geologists in the search for, and evaluation of beryllium deposits of the pegmatitic type.

It is known that, in his texture-paragenetic classification, K. A. Vlasov starts from the analysis of the interrelations between the main rock-forming minerals of the pegmatites (feldspar and quartz) and then distinguishes four types of

Table 17 | *Zonal classification of beryl-bearing granitic pegmatites*

ZONES AND REPLACEMENT COMPLEXES	LOCATION AND NATURE OF DEVELOPMENT IN THE PEGMATITE	STRUCTURE AND SIZE OF SEGREGATIONS OF ROCK-FORMING MINERALS	ROCK-FORMING MINERALS
(a) Zone of pegmatoid granite.	Outer zone of some streaky pegmatites. Sometimes the main or entire mass of intruded veins in the roots of pegmatite injections.	Granitic. From 0.5 to 10–15 cm feldspar phenocrysts.	Quartz, microcline and quartz, plagioclase.
(b) Zone of aplite-like pegmatite.	Thin fringe, developed continuously or in sections in the endo-contact of the pegmatite where there is no zone (a). Particularly characteristic of intruded pegmatites.	Fine-granular (aplitic, grano-blastic).	Quartz, oligoclase, microcline.
(c) Zone of graphic pegmatite.	Continuous zone or sections among medium-grained pegmatite in the outer part of pegmatites. Sometimes the whole mass of pegmatite.	Graphic. Quartz from 0.3 to 2 cm along the c-axis.	Quartz (22–30%), microcline (70–75%), or quartz (28–39%), oligoclase (57–71%).
(d) Zone of medium-grained and coarse-grained pegmatite.	In essentially graphic pegmatites—in central portions of pegmatites. In block pegmatites—in the outer part.	Apographic, pegmatoid. From 1 to 10 cm.	Quartz-microcline-perthite, or quartz-oligoclase, or quartz-oligoclase-microcline. In many pegmatites granular albite is substituted for the microcline of the zone.
(e) Zone of small-block pegmatite.	In the central part of pegmatites of block structure, or around the central core of veins; composed of block quartz.	Block. From 0.1 to 1 m.	Quartz-microcline-perthite (orthoclase-perthite) or quartz-oligoclase.
(f) Zone of block microcline (block plagioclase).	Large blocks, rarely a solid belt round segregations of block quartz in the center of the vein. Less frequently thick blocks in quartz in the central part of the pegmatite.	Block, giant-crystalline. From 1 to 10 m and more.	Microcline-perthite (orthoclase-perthite). In the group of plagioclase pegmatites—oligoclase to andesine.

CHARACTERISTIC TYPOMORPHIC MINERALS	RELATIONSHIP TO OTHER ZONES	RARE-EARTH MINERALS	IMPORTANCE FOR RARE METALS
Biotite, magnetite.	Gradual transitions into porphyritic granite and the zone of graphic pegmatite are known.	Monazite, allanite (as accessory minerals).	Absent in pegmatites interesting from commercial viewpoint. In prospecting the presence of pegmatites of this type only indicates the absence of rare metals.
Biotite, magnetite, black tourmaline, garnet, muscovite, cordierite.	Usually has a sharp contact with inner zones of the pegmatite. In replaced modifications often albitized. Differs from the outwardly similar fine-grained albite replacement complex in the composition of accessory minerals and of the rock-forming feldspar.	Minerals characteristic of inner zones can occur as single grains.	The product of reaction between the pegmatitic melt and the enclosing rocks in the early stages of crystallization. A strong development of the aplitic-pegmatite zone showing no trace of replacement is, in general, an unfavorable prospecting feature as regards rare metals.
Biotite, magnetite, garnet, muscovite after biotite.	Passes gradually into the zone of medium-grained pegmatite of apographic structure. On albitization commonly preserves the relict graphic structure.	As a rule, does not contain rare-earth minerals. The latter may be introduced in the process of albitization of the zone.	Strong development of graphic zone showing no trace of replacement processes is an unfavorable prospecting feature as regards rare metals.
Muscovite, black tourmaline. In the oligoclase modifications—magnetite, ilmenite.	Related by gradual transitions to the zone of graphic pegmatite. Passes also gradually into small-block pegmatite. On incomplete albitization usually preserves the relict apographic structure.	Sometimes contains beryl (more frequently in negligible quantities). The proportion of beryl increases in the albitized sections of the zone.	The presence of the medium-grained pegmatite zone containing traces of the albitization processes and very small proportions of rare-metal minerals points to the possibility of finding higher concentrations of these minerals in the block zones, especially in bulges and domes of pegmatites.
Do.	Connected by gradual transition with the preceding and two following zones.	Beryl, columbite-tantalite—in pocket-like accumulations. In plagioclase modifications—ilmenite.	Pegmatites with a central part of the zone of block pegmatite (without full differentiation into the zones of block quartz and microcline) are characterized in a number of cases by a commercial content of beryl, but, as a rule, are small-scale deposits.
As a rule, mono-mineralic. Sometimes small inclusions of quartz, usually regularly oriented.	Connected with zone (d) through small block pegmatite. An abrupt boundary with block quartz; idiomorphism of block microcline is usually observed with regard to block quartz.	At the boundary between block microcline and block quartz—agglomerates of beryl, tantalite-columbite, samarskite etc. In oligoclase and oligoclase-microcline modifications—gadolinite.	Wide development of block microcline in the pegmatite is a positive exploration feature enabling it to be isolated for a more detailed study.

Table 17 | *Zonal classification of beryl-bearing granitic pegmatites (cont.)*

ZONES AND REPLACEMENT COMPLEXES	LOCATION AND NATURE OF DEVELOPMENT IN THE PEGMATITE	STRUCTURE AND SIZE OF SEGREGATIONS OF ROCK-FORMING MINERALS	ROCK-FORMING MINERALS
(g) Zone of block quartz.	Large blocks, lenses, solid core in the central part of bodies. Sometimes occurs in fractures which intersect earlier zones, especially the zone of block microcline.	Block (massive). From 1 to 10 m and more.	Mainly monomineralic. Sometimes includes large idiomorphic crystals and blocks of microcline.
(h) Quartz-spodumene zone.	Lenses or solid core in the central part of pegmatites. Sometimes around a central core composed of block quartz.	Giant-crystalline. Spodumene from 0.1 to 10 m along the long axis.	Quartz, spodumene. Usually albite as secondary replacement mineral.
(i) Muscovite replacement complex: (1) quartz-muscovite complex (zone). (2) albite-muscovite complex (zone).	At the boundary between the quartz blocks (or quartz core) and the zones (c), (d), (f); also near the contacts, along fractures and pockets in zones (d) and (f). Rarely between the zone of block microcline and zone (d).	Granular-lamellar, medium-lamellar, to coarse-lamellar (1–20 cm), massive-lamellar.	Muscovite, quartz (with a small proportion of albite and relics of microcline) in weakly albitized modifications. Muscovite, albite (in albitized modifications).
(j) Albite replacement complex: (1) cleavelandite complex (zone). (2) fine granular albite complex (zone of saccharoidal or fine-lamellar albite).	Around the quartz-spodumene zone or the zone of block quartz; sometimes segregates in the vein parts adjacent to the contacts; develops as solid zone or in sections. Commonly related to fractures.	1. Lamellar, radial-lamellar (0.5–3 cm). 2. Fine-lamellar (0.1–0.5 cm). Fine-granular (up to 0.1 cm). Under the microscope granular-prismatic, prismatic, fluid-prismatic, bostonitic, fluid-bostonitic.	1. Cleavelandite, quartz. 2. Saccharoidal or fine-lamellar albite with or without quartz. Relics of microcline common.
(k) Lepidolite replacement complex: (1) quartz-lepidolite complex (zone). (2) albite-lepidolite complex (zone).	Central portions of pegmatites. Commonly in apical loci.	From fine to medium-lamellar.	Lepidolite, albite, quartz.
(l) Greisen replacement complex.	In various parts of the bodies. Near the quartz core or at the selvages. Sometimes related to fracturing.	Do.	Muscovite, albite, quartz.

CHARACTERISTIC TYPOMORPHIC MINERALS	RELATIONSHIP TO OTHER ZONES	RARE-EARTH MINERALS	IMPORTANCE FOR RARE METALS
As a rule, mono-mineralic. Sometimes near the boundary with block microcline, crystals of triphylite, apatite and rare-metal minerals.	Has sharp boundaries with zone (f). Sometimes connected by gradual transition with small-block pegmatite.	At the boundary with block microcline are quartz-crystals and pockets of beryl, columbite-tantalite, samarskite, etc.	Thick zone of block quartz, segregated in the shape of a core or axis in the pegmatite, is a positive exploration feature, especially when a thick zone of block microcline is present.
	Commonly a gradual transition to the zone of block quartz.	Alkali beryl (rosterite, vorobyevite), columbite-tantalite, microlite.	An ore zone for spodumene and a very positive exploration feature for the presence of rare-metal minerals in other zones.
Phosphates of iron and manganese, sulphides.	Replaces the feldspars of the zones (d), (e), (f).	Green and bluish-green beryl, columbite-tantalite.	In a number of places contains commercial concentrations of beryl, less often columbite-tantalite. Sections of the zone at the boundary between block quartz and block microcline, are commonly an economic ore-zone of beryl.
1. Greenish muscovite, green tourmaline, lithiophilite and secondary phosphates of iron and manganese, spessartite. 2. (a) Greenish muscovite, phosphates of iron and manganese. (b) Fine crystals of almandine-spessartite or fine needle-shaped crystals of black tourmaline.	On albitization of the zone of graphic or medium-grained pegmatite in a number of places the relict graphic or apographic structure is preserved due to the unreplaced quartz ingrowths. On replacement of the quartz-spodumene zone there forms a quartz-spodumene complex with the relict structure of the quartz-spodumene zone. The zone of block microcline is replaced completely in some places. Block quartz is usually replaced along fractures.	1. Alkali beryl (rosterite, vorobyevite) of white or rose color, columbite-tantalite, microlite. 2. Yellowish fine-crystalline beryl, columbite-tantalite.	Wide development of albitization is a very favorable feature in exploration and evaluation of pegmatites for the content of rare metals.
Rubellite, achroite.	Forms after zones (g) and (j), and especially after the quartz-spodumene zone.	Rosterite, vorobyevite, columbite-tantalite, microlite, pollucite.	The presence of the lepidolite zone points to a wide development of the replacement processes and is a very positive feature in prospecting for rare metals.
—	Forms in the replacement of the albite complex of block microcline and quartz.	Columbite-tantalite.	Manifestation of greisenization in pegmatites is a positive feature when prospecting for tantalite-columbite.

pegmatites, each of which is a natural genetical continuation of the preceding one (Fig. 13).

The first type—graphic and uniformly granular—is represented by a rock which consists completely, or almost completely of graphic pegmatite or of the uniformly granular pegmatite of granitic structure.

The second type—the block type—has two zones. The outer zone is composed of a pegmatite of graphic structure or else a medium-grained pegmatite of granitic structure. The central part consists of large feldspar crystals and of quartz blocks. The replacement processes take place in this type as indicated by the presence of mica and albite which develop after microcline.

The third type is fully differentiated (zoned). It is characterized by the presence of three main pegmatite-forming zones: (1) outer zones which, as in the preceding types, consist of a pegmatite of graphic or granitic structure; (2) middle zone which consists almost completely of potassium-sodium feldspars —usually microcline, sometimes oligoclase, and (3) central zone which is represented by segregations of massive quartz of different, often oval, form.

The fourth type, that containing rare metals, is characterized by the combination of the three zones referred to above with an independent replacement zone composed mainly of albite and muscovite and of other minerals formed during the replacement stage.

It should be noted that all of the more or less important beryl deposits in pegmatites are related to the third and fourth types of Vlasov's classification. This classification is, therefore, of great importance as far as exploration and valuation of beryl deposits is concerned.

The experience gained during the last decade with pegmatitic beryllium deposits showed that the study of the inner horizontal and vertical zoning of pegmatites is of great importance in their evaluation and exploration. Unless the characteristic regularities expressed in the zonality of beryl-bearing pegmatites are taken into account, it is impossible to estimate correctly the prospects of the deposit and to determine the suitable direction of geological exploration.

Let us deal briefly with the zonal characteristics of the beryl-bearing pegmatites.

We define the zone of a pegmatitic body as a spatial separation of a mineral aggregate which is formed at a certain stage of the pegmatitic process (paragenetic complex). Each zone has its own qualitative and quantitative properties: (1) the qualitative mineralogical composition; (2) structure; (3) the quantitative relations between the minerals and the ensuing chemical composition.

A zone is not a constant formation: in the course of the pegmatitic process it changes from incipient nest-like segregations to a continuous zone in the pegmatitic body. Subsequent processes can result in a complete or partial remaking of the zone, traces of its existence being preserved in the form of relics

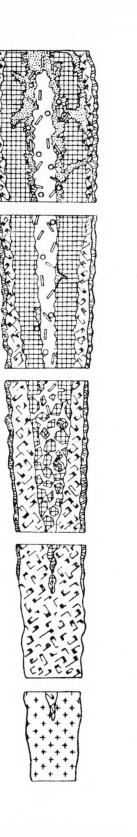

Fig. 13. Scheme of the texture-paragenetic types of granitic pegmatites (according to Vlasov, 1952). (1) Granite; (2) pegmatite of graphic and granite structures; (3) microcline, oligoclase, and microcline-spodumene zones, also blocks and belts of late quartz; (4) quartz blocks, cores, and crystals; (5) replacement zone (cleavelandite, muscovite, beryl tantalite, spodumene, etc.); (6) crystals of rare-metal minerals (spodumene, beryl, etc.); (7) muscovite-quartz-albite zones and fringes.

in the replacement zone. In all types of granitic pegmatites one observes a distinct relationship between the rare-metal (including beryllium) minerals and certain paragenetic complexes, as demonstrated in Table 17 (zonal classification of granitic pegmatites).

The nature of zonal development makes it possible to distinguish six main paragenetic groups of beryl-bearing granitic pegmatites (Table 18).

MIAROLITIC STREAKY (SYNGENETIC) PEGMATITES. These mostly occur in the endo-contact part of the pegmatite-bearing granite intrusions; they have, as a rule, small dimensions, an irregular form, and no distinct contacts with the enclosing granite.

The outer zone of pegmatites of this group is usually composed of graphic pegmatite which passes, in the central part into coarse-grained pegmatite of pegmatoid structure. In the coarse-grained, and less frequently in the graphic pegmatite, one finds drusy cavities containing well-formed crystals of feldspars,

Table 18 | *Nature of zonality variation in different groups of beryl-bearing granitic pegmatites*

GROUPS	ZONE OF GRAPHIC PEGMATITE	ZONE OF MEDIUM- AND COARSE-GRAINED PEGMATITE	ZONE OF BLOCK PEGMATITE	ZONE OF BLOCK MICROCLINE	ZONE OF BLOCK QUARTZ
Graphic and cognate medium-grained biotite-microcline pegmatites (including syngenetic miarolitic pegmatites).	Predominant development.	Rudimentary development.	Absent.	Absent.	Absent.
Block biotite-microcline and biotite-plagioclase-microcline pegmatites.	Weak or normal development.	Weak or normal development.	Normal or predominant development.	Weak or normal development.	Normal development.
Block and fully-differentiated muscovite-microcline pegmatites.	Weak development. Commonly absent. May be albitized with preservation of structure.	Normal development.	Development from normal to weak.	Predominant development.	
Replaced muscovite-albite pegmatite.	Are replaced partly or completely, or are absent.		Partly or completely replaced.		Normal development.
Replaced spodumene-albite pegmatites.	Are replaced partly or completely, or are absent.		Predominant or normal development, partly (less often completely) replaced.		
Replaced lepidolite-albite pegmatites.	Do.		Normal development; usually strongly or completely replaced.		

quartz, beryl, tourmaline, and topaz. From the practical viewpoint, the miarolitic pegmatites are interesting only as a source of precious and colored stones. No commercial accumulations of beryl are known to exist in the pegmatites of this group.

BLOCK AND FULLY-DIFFERENTIATED BIOTITE-MICROCLINE PEGMATITES. These pegmatites, containing rare-earth minerals, are a fairly widespread type, but only very few of such pegmatites contain gadolinite or beryl.

The block and fully-differentiated biotite-microcline pegmatites containing higher concentrations of rare-earth minerals usually occur in the fractures of ultra-basic rocks and in various gneisses near to the contacts of large granite intrusions of pre-Cambrian age, or else directly in the fractures of the endo-contact zone of the same intrusions. The outer zone of pegmatitic bodies consists in the most general case of the graphic (sometimes medium-grained) quartz-microcline or quartz-oligoclase pegmatite; nearer to the center one finds the zone of block pegmatite, which encloses the central quartz core of the pegmatitic body. Accumulations of coarse-lamellar biotite occur at the bound-

QUARTZ-SPODUMENE ZONE	MUSCOVITE REPLACEMENT COMPLEX (ZONE)	ALBITE REPLACEMENT COMPLEX (ZONE)	LEPIDOLITE REPLACEMENT COMPLEX (ZONE)	GREISEN REPLACEMENT COMPLEX (ZONE)
Absent; may be present in rudimentary form in the druses of miarolitic pegmatites.			Absent.	
Absent.	Absent, or rudimentary development.		Absent.	Do.
Absent.	Wide development.	Weak development, though individual sections can be substantially albitized.	Do.	
Absent or rudimentary development.	Do.	Predominant development.		Develops here and there in the apical portions of pegmatitic bodies.
Strong development (to predominant).		Wide development to predominant.	Rudimentary to weak development.	Do.
Weak development; usually replaced.	Weak development; usually replaced.	Do.	Normal development.	Absent.

ary between the quartz core and the block segregations of microcline. Pockets of biotite are also scattered in the outer zones of the pegmatite. Muscovite is found in a number of places near the boundary with the block quartz, but it occurs only in a very subordinate quantity. Gadolinite (less frequently beryl) occurs usually in the peripheral portions of the quartz core or in the block feldspar near its boundary with the quartz core. Gadolinite is usually closely associated with biotite. Thalenite, fergusonite, samarskite and other tantalo-niobates of yttria are encountered in paragenesis with gadolinite.

As regards the beryllium content, this type has no economic significance in view of the rare occurrence and small sizes of the deposits; there are, however, known examples of commercial mining of gadolinite from such pegmatites with a view to extracting rare earths of the yttrium group. In southern Norway (areas of Iveland and Setersdalen) gadolinite was mined simultaneously with the working of pegmatites for ceramic raw material; in the U.S.A. (deposit Baringer Hill, Texas) gadolinite was obtained from a large pegmatitic body characterized by an abnormally high content of rare-earth minerals. It should be noted that in both cases the total amount of the mined material was extremely small as a beryllium raw material.

BLOCK AND FULLY-DIFFERENTIATED MUSCOVITE-MICROCLINE PEG-MATITES. These usually occur in metamorphosed rocks (most frequently in the crystalline schists of the exo-contact zone of the pegmatite-bearing granite intrusions), or else they lie directly between the granites, occurring frequently in contraction and shear fractures developed in the apical part of the intrusions.

The internal structure of pegmatitic formations of this group is characterized by fairly constant common features (see Figs. 15–17), although there exist numerous differences in details.

At the contact between the pegmatite and the enclosing rocks one observes (but not always) a usually thin aplite-like fringe formed as a result of the physico-chemical reaction between the pegmatite melt and the enclosing rocks. The following outer zone of the pegmatite consists of the graphic and medium-grained pegmatite, viz. the graphic pegmatite either occupies the outermost part of the pegmatitic body, passing further into the medium-grained pegmatite of apographic structure or else it occurs in the form of individual areas in the preponderant mass of medium-grained pegmatite. Depending on the degree of differentiation of the pegmatitic body, the medium- and coarse-grained pegmatite zone passes, towards the center, either into the zone of block pegmatite, composed of giant crystal-blocks of microcline-perthite and large quartz blocks, or else into the monomineralic zone of block microcline. In the former case the central part of the pegmatitic body is a zone of block pegmatite or a practically

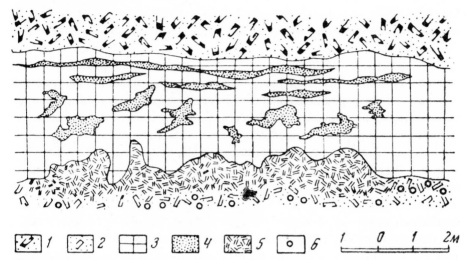

Fig. 14. Beryl in the albitized medium-grained pegmatite near the zone of block microcline. (1) Medium-grained pegmatite of apographic structure; (2) same, but partly albitized; (3) block microcline-perthite; (4) block quartz; (5) quartz-muscovite replacement complex; (6) beryl.

monomineralic quartz core; in the latter case a quartz core occurs in most places (in rare cases the core consists of block microcline-perthite).

The muscovite replacement zone (quartz-muscovite or quartz-albite-muscovite replacement complex) develops usually between the quartz core and the surrounding feldspar zones, viz. either in separate sections or as a continuous fringe. In a number of places one observes a noticeable albitization of block microcline and especially of medium-grained pegmatite, but the primary apographic structure of the latter is always preserved.

In the pegmatites of this group beryl is mainly concentrated at the boundary between the central block-quartz zone and the surrounding zone of block microcline or medium-grained pegmatite. Less frequently the beryl crystals occur directly in block[5] quartz and still more rarely in the block microcline at some distance from the quartz core. In individual cases increased concentrations of beryl, associated with muscovite in the replacement complex are observed at the boundary between the block pegmatite (or block microcline) zone and the zone of the partly albitized medium-grained pegmatite of apographic structure (Fig. 14).

The beryl-bearing ore zone occurring usually along the periphery of the quartz core commonly includes nests of the muscovite replacement complex.

[5] The term 'block' is used here not in the ordinary morphological sense, but for describing a definite generation of quartz or microcline, which occupies a definite place in the pegmatitic process.

In paragenesis with beryl one usually finds large well-formed crystals of columbite-tantalite, triphylite, graftonite, and less frequently samarskite and zircon.

The chief characteristic of the block muscovite-microcline pegmatites is the coarsely-crystalline variety of beryl, with a low alkali content. Beryl of this type has well-developed hexagonal crystals of a long-prismatic habit, sometimes with a complex termination. In different deposits the color of the crystals varies from blue (aquamarine) to green and brown. The most commonly occurring are beryls of light green and yellowish-green color. The crystal dimensions vary from a few centimeters to 1.2–2 m (rarely more) along the c-axis, and from fractions of one centimeter to 1 meter across. In most deposits the mean size of crystals is not less than 2 × 5 cm, which enables their beneficiation to be carried out in the simplest way by hand picking. In such deposits crystals of less than 0.5 cm along the c-axis are rather an exception, and therefore almost all the beryl which has not been crushed during mining can be picked by hand.

From the practical viewpoint a very important characteristic of this variety of beryl is its highly irregular distribution in pockets in the ore zone which forms a border round the quartz core of the pegmatite. At the same time the larger the crystals or nests of crystals the more pronounced the non-uniform distribution of beryl in the ore zone. In the mining of beryl deposits of this type one frequently encounters places when several tons of beryl concentrate were obtained from one pocket consisting of one or a few large beryl crystals, whereas subsequent mining along a distance of several dozens of meters was carried out in a barren or almost barren rock, until another pocket was reached.

Somewhat different properties are found in the alkali (sodium) beryl variety which occurs less frequently in the block muscovite-microcline pegmatites. The crystals of sodium beryl, which have a characteristic cone-shaped or pyramidal habit and poorly-formed faces, are usually concentrated: (1) at the boundary between the zones of the block and medium-grained pegmatites occurring in the albitized and muscovitized medium-grained pegmatite of apographic structure, and (2) at the boundary between the zones of block quartz and block microcline, occurring in the albitized microcline. Unlike the previous alkali-free beryl whose crystals usually do not contain any foreign inclusions, the sodium beryl commonly forms so-called 'stuffed' crystals whose central part is stuffed with albitized medium-grained pegmatite, albite, quartz, and muscovite. Instances of irregular intergrowth of beryl with quartz and albite also are not rare. The color of sodium beryl varies from pale-green to yellowish-green and greenish-white. The crystal dimensions vary roughly within the same limits as referred to above for the alkali-free variety, although giant crystals, extending for over 1 m along the c-axis, are met with much less frequently.

A characteristic feature of the sodium variety of the beryl is its more uniform distribution in the beryl-bearing zone, which is particularly true of the relatively small crystals connected with the albitized portions of the medium-grained pegmatite (at the boundary with the block zone). It should be noted that the presence, in the sodium beryl, of inter-grown albite and quartz may cause difficulties in obtaining an acceptable concentrate by hand picking. The conventional hand cleaning of crystals by crushing results in considerable losses in the fines.

The thickness of the beryl-bearing ore-body in the mined deposits of the block muscovite-microcline pegmatites varies from 0.5 to 2 m (rarely more), depending on the dimensions and morphology of the pegmatitic bodies. The thickest and most constant ore zones are observed in large, well-differentiated pegmatitic bodies of isometric or lenticular shape.

According to published data the beryl content in commercially valuable pegmatites of this type varies between 0.2 and 0.5 percent, rarely exceeding the latter limit.

When the beryl content is low (below 0.25 percent) and when its distribution is highly irregular, the mining of the block muscovite-microcline pegmatites for beryl commonly proves unprofitable. In this connection special attention should be paid to the by-production of a number of useful constituents (widely applied in foreign countries), which highly increases the profitableness of their exploitation (mica, feldspar, quartz, rare-earth minerals).

For the type of deposit under consideration the common association is beryl and columbite-tantalite. In a number of deposits beryl is also mined as a by-product when pegmatites are exploited for muscovite or ceramic raw materials.

In many places, when the block and fully-differentiated muscovite-microcline pegmatites are mined in depth, one observes an increase in the thickness of the zone of graphic and medium-grained pegmatite, associated with a corresponding decrease in thickness of the block zones (Fig. 15). At the same time the general decrease in the degree of differentiation of the pegmatite is accompanied by a noticeable drop in the beryl content, down to its complete disappearance. The zonal variation with beryl content at greater depths is the more pronounced the weaker the differentiation of the examined surface horizon of the pegmatitic body. One should, however, make the reservation that the observed tendency towards the change of zonality depends entirely on the nature of the erosional cut-off of the pegmatite. In cases when the erosional cut-off opens up the apical portion of the pegmatite whose thickness increases with depth, one often observes a converse picture of zonal change, i.e. the poorly-differentiated pegmatite at depth changes, as the thickness increases, into large-block or even fully-differentiated pegmatite with a higher beryl concentration than at the surface. (See, for example, the Big pegmatite, Alstead, New Hampshire, U.S.A., Fig. 16.)

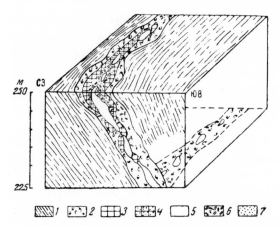

Fig. 15. Block-diagram of the lens-shaped body of the block muscovite-microcline pegmatite characterized by a decrease of the degree of differentiation along the dip. (1) Schists; (2) medium-grained pegmatite; (3) block microcline-perthite; (4) block microcline, albitized; (5) block quartz; (6) muscovite; (7) albite.

The block muscovite-microcline pegmatites with beryl are known and mined in most beryl-bearing pegmatitic fields of the world. By far the majority of deposits were worked only in open-casts, because the irregular distribution and, in general, the low beryl content, made the deep mining of the pegmatitic ore-bodies unprofitable. Only a few of the biggest deposits of this kind were mined to a depth of 40–60 m. As an example of these beryl-bearing pegmatites we can describe the Big pegmatite (Gilsum and Victory Mines, Alstead, N.H., U.S.A.) (Fig. 16), which out-crops on the surface as a thick (ca. 30 m) vein composed of medium- and coarse-grained microcline-quartz-plagioclase pegmatite with biotite. At a depth of 30 m from the surface the pegmatite forms a swell whose thickness (at a depth of 50 m from the surface) is more than 60 m. The central portion of the swell is a zone of the block quartz-microcline pegmatite (thickness about 50 m), containing pockets of beryl. Muscovite occurs in some portions between the block zone and the medium-grained pegmatite. The thinner plagioclase-muscovite zone occurs also along the north western contact of the pegmatite with the enclosing quartz-mica schists. The Big pegmatite has been mined for many years, and is now being mined at a depth of over 50 m.

Less frequent are deposits represented by fully-differentiated pegmatites which have an independent monomineralic zone consisting of block microcline-perthite. Such beryl deposits are characterized by a comparatively large and constant size of the ore zone. Examples are known of deposits of this group having been mined to a depth of 40–80 m along the dip; in many cases fully-differentiated pegmatite is replaced at depth by block pegmatite.

A similar transition can be illustrated by a number of examples; Figure 15 shows a section through one of the typical veins.

The vein has a lenticular form and is conformable with the enclosing quartz-biotite schists in which it can be traced for a distance of about 100 m. In the most mineralized part of the vein its thickness attains 12 m. Along the contact between the vein and the enclosing schists one traces a thin aplite-like fringe that alternates with an external zone represented by medium-grained quartz-microcline pegmatite, in places fairly strongly albitized. The central portion of the vein at the outcrop is composed mainly of giant (<4 m across), strongly albitized microcline-perthite blocks. Quartz blocks that appear here and there in the block microcline zone are always of small dimensions and are surrounded by thick quartz-albite-muscovite fringes.

The beryl (sodium variety) encountered in the outcrop is characterized by a white color and by the conoid form of crystals which most commonly occur in albitized microcline.

At a depth of 5 m below the surface, the vein is a solid zone of block quartz (3 m thick), surrounded by a muscovite zone which is particularly thick (1.5 m) in the hanging-wall of the pegmatitic body. The block microcline zone that forms a solid belt around the entire central portion is strongly albitized and is transformed into a solid aggre-

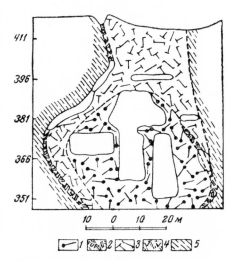

Fig. 16. Section of the Big pegmatite, Gilsum and Victory mines, Alstead, N.H., U.S.A. (according to E. N. Cameron et al., 1951). (1) Quartz-microcline-perthite (block) pegmatite (core); (2) muscovite-plagioclase-microcline-perthite pegmatite; (3) biotite-microcline-perthite-quartz-plagioclase pegmatite; (4) muscovite-quartz-plagioclase pegmatite; (5) quartz-schists.

gate of roughly lamellar albite. Here, one finds a concentration of very large crystals of beryl and columbite.

At the horizon examined, the color of beryl varies from white to greenish. Zoned crystals with a pale-green center and snow-white peripheral parts have been encountered. A characteristic feature of these crystals is the presence of numerous inclusions of black tourmaline, muscovite, and albite. Besides columbite, the beryl is associated with minerals of the phosphate group (triphylite, graftonite, arrojadite etc.) and cyrtolite.

The degree of differentiation of the pegmatite decreases gradually as depth increases; at the same time albitization decreases, and the beryl content drops noticeably. At a depth of 40 m along the dip the main mass of the pegmatite is composed of medium-grained pegmatite. The block-quartz zone consists here of separated blocks that become more abundant in the central part of the vein. Beryl in individual pale-green prismatic crystals (as much as 4 × 10 cm) and in druses, occurs in the peripheral parts of the quartz blocks, and also in the muscovite pockets encountered in the medium-grained pegmatite. The beryl content at the horizon 40 m below the surface is one-third of that at the well-differentiated surface horizon.

In the typical example above, the beryl-bearing ore zone, 1.5–2 m thick, was disposed around the quartz core of the pegmatite, enclosing the peripheral portions of block quartz. The ore zone, solid at the surface, split, as depth increased, into individual pockets that also are more numerous at the boundary of the block segregations of quartz.

A more complex distribution of beryl in the fully-differentiated muscovite-microcline pegmatites may be illustrated in the example of a large pegmatite whose formation took place under complex tectonic conditions that resulted in various peculiarities of its internal structure.

The pegmatitic body, which has the form of a dike with a tortuous boundary, occurs in quartz-biotite schists of Precambrian age, 500 m from the contact with the intrusion of two, mica granites. The strike of the pegmatite coincides with that of the metamorphic stratum, but down dip the dike, a typical stepped body (Fig. 17), intersects steeply-dipping schists at different (commonly gentle) angles. The dike was traced along the strike for 360 m; in its main part the true thickness varies between 20 m and 30 m.

The pegmatite type is determined by the preponderant development of the zones of block microcline and block quartz. The muscovitic replacement complex also is widely developed. Here and there one can observe a noticeable albitization of medium-grained pegmatite and of block microcline.

The flanks of the dike and its outermost zone are composed of medium-grained pegmatite of apographic structure, albitized to a large extent. The fundamental mass of the pegmatite is composed of a zone of block microcline-perthite, whose thickness in places exceeds 20 m. Individual portions of the zone, especially near the hanging-wall, and at the boundary with the block quartz, are strongly albitized.

The interrelations between block microcline and block quartz are highly interesting. Block quartz intersects the block-microcline zone along fractures which are roughly parallel to the trend of the pegmatite dike. In addition, vein-like formations of block quartz are present at the contact between pegmatite and the enclosing rocks and the large xenoliths in the central portion of the pegmatite.

Fairly large beryl crystals and crystal nests of commercial value have a close

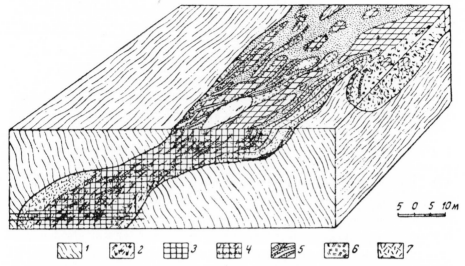

Fig. 17. Block diagram of a portion of a beryl-bearing pegmatite dike. Block quartz transgresses the zone of block microcline-perthite. (1) Quartz-biotite schists; (2) medium-grained pegmatite, albitized; (3) block microcline-perthite; (4) block microcline, albitized; (5) block quartz; (6) muscovite; (7) albite replacement complex.

relationship to the vein-like segregations of quartz and are encountered (1) near the quartz apophyses and veins at the contact of pegmatite with large xenoliths of the enclosing rocks; (2) in the endo-contact zone of the pegmatite, near the vein-like quartz segregations; (3) in albitized microcline between quartz veins which intersect it; and (4) directly in the streaky segregations of quartz.

Muscovite, triphylite, columbite, and zircon are found in albitized pegmatite in close association with beryl.

With increasing depth in the pegmatite there is a reduction in the amount and thickness of vein-like quartz segregations and an increase in thickness of the zone of medium-grained pegmatite.

REPLACED MUSCOVITE-ALBITE PEGMATITES. These are closely related through gradual transitions to the muscovite-microcline pegmatites referred to above and are characterized by the preponderant development of the albite zone superposed on the zone of block microcline and medium-grained pegmatite.

Depending on the specific geological conditions of the formation of deposits, the beryl-bearing albite zone is either arranged in the central part of the pegmatite around the quartz core, or else it is associated with the endo-contact, forming the outer zone of the pegmatite.

In the mass of the albite replacement complex one usually observes relics of block microcline and of albitized medium-grained pegmatite of apographic structure. At the same time the internal structure of such albitized pegmatites is fairly irregular in a number of places.

The most frequently occurring variety of beryl in the replaced muscovite-albite pegmatites is the alkali (sodium and sodium-lithium) type closely related to the albite replacement complex. Owing to its light (white) color and commonly irregular crystal form, this beryl is identified in many deposits only with difficulty. In addition to large crystals of conical, pyramidal, and irregular form, the alkali beryl in many places forms small crystals that do not lend themselves to hand picking.

The beryl-bearing ore zone in the replaced muscovite-albite pegmatites is always related to the albite replacement zone. The loci of beryl concentration in the pegmatite can be: the albite zone at the boundary with the quartz core; the albite zone near the contact with the enclosing rocks or with the xenoliths of enclosing rocks; and pockets of the quartz-muscovite and albite-muscovite replacement complex, scattered in the albite zone or occurring near the contact of the pegmatite.

In individual deposits one can observe a more or less uniform distribution of beryl in the albite zone. In this case the beryl crystals are usually small and lend themselves with difficulty to hand picking. It should be noted in general, that the group of beryl-bearing pegmatitic formations under consideration is characterized by a more uniform distribution of beryl and, in a number of places, by its greater abundance in the ore zone than is the case in the muscovite-nicrocline pegmatites with weak albitization. Besides the usual greenish muscovite, one usually finds in association with beryllium in the albite zone: the manganese garnet—spessartite, triphylite-lithiophilite, green tourmaline, and, of the useful constituents, columbite-tantalite (at times of great practical value), and cassiterite.

Thus the beryl deposits related to replaced muscovite-albite pegmatites are in most cases complex, viz. beryl-columbite, beryl-tantalite, or beryl-cassiterite ores.

A series of specific examples of deposits of this group are given below.

1. A beryl-bearing pegmatite body occurs in metamorphozed quartz-biotite schists 100 m from the contact of the metamorphic rocks with biotite granite. It has the form of an irregular vein with bulges; the vein in the bulges thickens to 8 m and thins to 1–1.5 m.

A characteristic feature of the described vein is a wide development of the albite replacement zone that conceals the original form of the pegmatite. In fact, almost all of the pegmatite is composed of white granular albite. The bulges of the albite vein contain as inclusions individual irregular quartz segregations and blocks, relics of microcline-perthite, and large books of greenish muscovite. In the central part of the pegmatite there is occasionally a zone of block quartz as much as 1 m thick. Block quartz is surrounded by fan-shaped packets of greenish-silvery muscovite. The extremities of the vein, and locally those portions adjacent to contacts, are composed of highly albitized, typical medium-grained pegmatite of apographic structure.

In the neighborhood of muscovite pockets which tend to be near the boundaries of quartz blocks, there are usually individual crystals and pockets of bluish-green beryl, from 1 to 10 cm across and as much as 20 cm long. The beryl crystals are fairly well shaped, and leave distinct replicas of faces in the albite.

Columbite-tantalite forms a peculiar herringbone pattern of lamellar crystals in albite that is in close association with beryl. The same areas are characterized by the presence of large crystals as much as 5 cm across of brown-yellow manganese garnet (spessartite), and of irregular segregations of bluish-grey apatite.

The beryllium content in the albite zone is 0.25 to 0.30 percent.

2. A pegmatite (Fig. 18) occurring in quartz-mica schists has the form of an irregular lens about 90 m long and is characterized by a thick (12 m) bulge on the west. The bulge is composed, for the most part, of solid block microcline among which individual small blocks of quartz and pocket-shaped segregations of amblygonite occur. The microcline is albitized to a large extent, and is intersected by streaks of an albite replacement complex containing the white sodium-lithium beryl, columbite, and large segregations of triphylite-lithiophilite. The eastern, thinner, part of the lens is entirely composed of an albite zone that contains relatively high concentrations of large conical crystals of white alkali-beryl. Light-brown manganese garnet (spessartite), rose lithiophilite, and columbite also are found with beryl in the beryl-bearing albite zone.

3. The pegmatite of the East Selden deposit, Conn., U.S.A. (Cameron and Shainen, 1947), which is a lenticular body lying conformably in metamorphosed schists, can be used as an example of replaced muscovite-albite pegmatites containing scattered beryl. The pegmatite, over 70 m long and 10 m thick, is composed mainly of a muscovite-quartz-albite aggregate (albite zone) containing scattered beryl crystals. In the albite zone there are scattered pocket-shaped areas consisting of block segregations of quartz and of microcline-perthite which also is albitized to a large extent. The richest aggregates of beryl crystals are related to these areas.

When replaced muscovite-albite pegmatites are mined in depth there is, in a number of places, a decrease in the extent of albitization and a transition into a partly-albitized block muscovite-microcline pegmatite. Such phenomena are described in the literature (Beus, 1951, 1953), where they are illustrated by

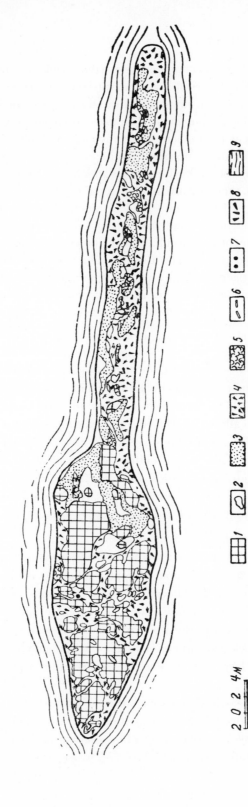

Fig. 18. Replaced muscovite-albite pegmatite with amblygonite and beryl. (1) Block microcline-perthite; (2) block quartz; (3) fine-grained albite; (4) cleavelandite; (5) greisen replacement complex; (6) amblygonite; (7) triphylite pockets; (8) beryl; (9) schists.

70

specific geological examples (Fig. 19). In other places the nature of the zonal change of the replaced muscovite-albite pegmatite at some depth, determined by the peculiarities of the pegmatite and its morphology, is more complex (Fig. 20, 21). In particular, the latter may be seen in the instance of the Old Mike pegmatite deposit referred to below.

The Old Mike pegmatite, Custer County, South Dakota, U.S.A. (Cameron et al., 1951) presents in plan a fairly regular pegmatite lens of over 100 m in length and up to 15 m thick in the bulge. The pegmatitic body is exposed vertically for over 50 m. It is also lens-shaped in the bulge, the lower part of the lens tapering to a vein about 2 m thick that continues in depth; it has not been followed to its final disappearance (see Fig. 21).

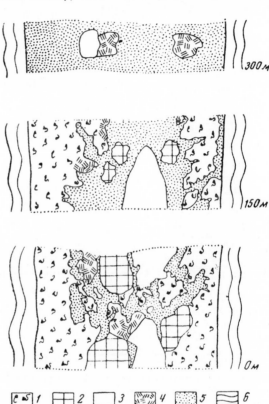

The pegmatite has a clear zonal structure. Its central part consists of a thick quartz core surrounded by a zone of block quartz-microcline pegmatite which is to a large extent albitized, while in the lower part of the lens (under the core) it is completely replaced by a quartz-cleavelandite assemblage. This is succeeded towards the margins of the lens by a thin albite-muscovite zone that grades in turn into the outer albite zone. The outer albite zone forms the portions of

Fig. 19. Transition of muscovite-albite pegmatite with depth into block muscovite-microcline pegmatite. (1) Medium-grained quartz-microcline pegmatite; (2) block microcline-perthite; (3) block quartz; (4) quartz-muscovite replacement complex; (5) albite replacement complex; (6) schists.

the lens adjacent to contacts and the apex of the body, as well as the lead vein which continues into depth where a new bulge is possible.

Beryl is mainly related to the segregations of the quartz-muscovite replacement complex, which occur near the core in the albitized and muscovitized portions.

REPLACED SPODUMENE-ALBITE AND LEPIDOLITE-ALBITE PEGMATITES. These differ from the muscovite-albite pegmatites referred to above in that they contain considerable concentrations of spodumene or lepidolite. The crystals of spodumene are usually encountered in the quartz core of the pegmatite

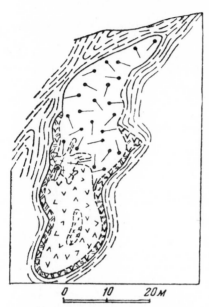

(quartz-spodumene zone), which is often albitized to a large extent (quartz-albite-spodumene zone). A characteristic feature of the pegmatites of this group is an intense development of albitization and commonly a pronounced concentric zonality.

The albite zone, in many places composed of cleavelandite, usually lies around the central quartz-spodumene pegmatite core. This zone contains white (less frequently colorless or rose) alkali-beryl scattered in cleavelandite in the form of irregular or short-prismatic crystals. Beryl usually is most abundant at the boundary between the albite zone and the quartz-spodumene pegmatite core. The characteristic accessory minerals of the beryl-containing albite zone are: greenish muscovite, spessartite, green tourmaline, lithiophilite, and amblygonite. In a series of deposits one finds the following minerals in association with beryl: mangano-columbite, mangano-tantalite, microlite, and cassiterite. The white or greenish-white alkali-beryl (the sodium or sodium-lithium variety) can also be present in the outer albitized zones of the pegmatitic body. The distribution and nature of beryl connected with the outer zones are identical with those in the replaced muscovite-albite pegmatites.

Fig. 20. Section through the Strickland-Cramer pegmatite (intensification of albitization with depth is characteristic), Portland, Connecticut, U.S.A. (after E. N. Cameron et al., 1951). (1) Cleavelandite-quartz pegmatite; (2) solid quartz (core); (3) quartz-plagioclase pegmatite (albite zone); (4) plagioclase-quartz-microcline-perthite pegmatite with sections of graphic pegmatite (partial albitization is seen); (5) muscovite quartz-plagioclase pegmatite; (6) schists.

All beryl occurrences in replaced spodumene-albite pegmatites are complex beryl-spodumene or beryl-tantalite (columbite)-spodumene deposits. In a series of deposits microlite and cassiterite are additional ore-minerals.

In many spodumene-albite pegmatites there are rudimentary replacement formations of lepidolite or greisen which usually increase with decrease in depth of the pegmatite. The increase of the lepidolite or greisen zone governs the transition to the replaced lepidolite-albite or to the relatively rare greisen-albite pegmatites.

LEPIDOLITE-ALBITE PEGMATITES. These are characterized by a wide development of the lepidolite zone (quartz-lepidolite or albite-lepidolite replacement complexes) which usually occurs in the central part of the pegmatite. At the same time the spodumene-containing zones are either present or else are in a subordinated position. Segregations of the rose-colored (vorobyevite), or colorless and transparent (rosterite) lithium or lithium-caesium alkali-beryl are usually related to the lepidolite replacement complex. Rose-colored, colorless or polychromous tourmaline is the characteristic accessory mineral of the zone. Of the rare-metal minerals the following are associated with beryl: microlite, manganotantalite, stibio-tantalite, cassiterite, and pollucite. As in the case of the spodumene-albite pegmatites, the central lepidolite zone is usually surrounded by an albite (cleavelandite) zone which is followed by the outer zones of the pegmatite, commonly albitized to a greater or lesser extent. As in the case of previously analyzed varieties of replaced pegmatites, the individual outer zones may be beryl-bearing.

As with the spodumene-albite pegmatites, all beryl deposits related to the replaced lepidolite-albite pegmatites are complex. The following useful metals can be extracted from the type under discussion; lithium (lepidolite, spodumene, amblygonite); niobium and tantalum (mangano-columbite, mangano-tantalite, microlite), beryllium (beryl), caesium (pollucite), and tin (cassiterite).

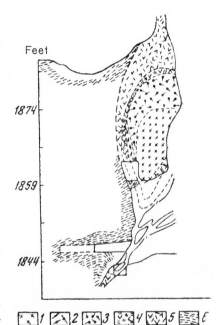

Fig. 21. Section through the Old Mike pegmatite, Custer County, South Dakota, U.S.A. (after Cameron et al., 1951). (1) Quartz core; (2) quartz-cleavelandite pegmatite; (3) albite-quartz-microcline-perthite pegmatite; (4) muscovite quartz-albite pegmatite; (5) quartz-muscovite-albite pegmatite; (6) quartz-mica schists.

When replaced spodumene-albite and lepidolite-albite pegmatites are mined in depth, one can notice a zonal change shown by the substitution of spodumene-albite or muscovite-albite pegmatite for the lepidolite-albite (or greisen-albite) pegmatite.

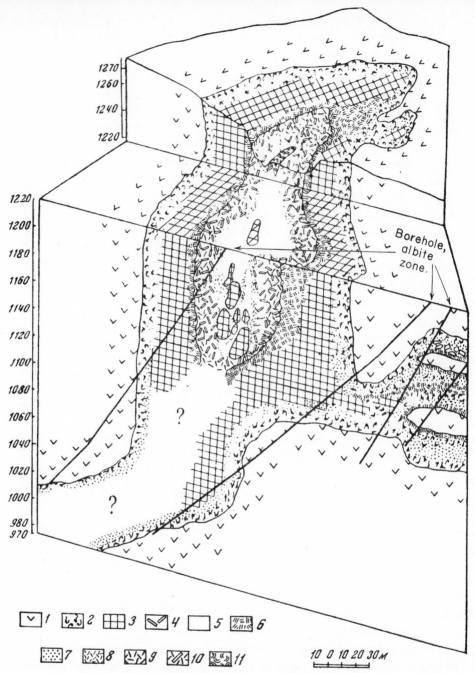

Fig. 22. Block-diagram of a large stock of replaced spodumene-albite pegmatite with clear zoning. (1) Gabbro; (2) zone of the albitized medium-grained pegmatite of apographic structure; (3) zone of block microcline; (4) quartz-spodumene zone; (5) zone of block quartz; (6) muscovite zone (quartz-muscovite replacement complex); (7) medium-grained saccharoidal albite; (8) fine-grained finely-lamellar albite; (9) cleavelandite complex (with finely-lamellar albite); (10) quartz-spodumene-cleavelandite complex; (11) lepidolite zone.

Characteristic examples of beryl-bearing pegmatites of the group under discussion are quoted below.

1. A very large pegmatitic deposit of spodumene and beryl is associated with a mass of basic rocks of gabbro composition, which is a large xenolith in the granite-intrusion roof. The structure of the deposit is determined by the presence of the gabbro of two main fracture systems that control the distribution and morphological peculiarities of pegmatites within the limits of the section.

The former system consists of gently-dipping fractures trending northwest and dipping towards the southwest. The fractures of the latter system are characterized by steep (at times nearly vertical) angles of dip, and have roughly the same trend as the fractures of the former system.

Stepped veins or the rarer gently-dipping veins with thick stock-shaped bulges are related to the areas where the fracture systems referred to above intersect one another. The bulges form as a result of the relative displacement of blocks in the area where two or more fracture systems intersect each other.

One of the gently-dipping veins with a thick dome-shaped bulge having the form of a stock with an elliptical section in plan, is a characteristic example of replaced spodumene-albite pegmatites with beryl, tantalite, and microlite.

The stock-shaped bulge is 250 × 150 m in area and has a very well developed concentric zonality that is preserved down the dip to a depth of over 200 m (Fig. 22). From the contacts to the center one can distinguish in the stock the zone of graphic pegmatite and medium-grained apographic pegmatite (partly albitized), the zone of pockets of saccharoidal albite, the block microcline zone, the quartz-muscovite zone, the spodumene-cleavelandite zone, the quartz-spodumene zone, the zone of pockets of finely-lamellar albite, the core of block quartz with large blocks of microcline-perthite, and the lepidolite zone (developed only in upper horizons of the stock) (Table 19).

The main beryl-bearing zone of the pegmatite is the zone of pockets of saccharoidal albite. In the zone under discussion, the light-green and yellowish-green beryl which usually forms prismatic crystals with poorly defined faces preferentially developed, are commonly highly corroded with albite. The size of the crystals varies from very small to 3 × 10 cm. Beryl is distributed in pockets in the zone; its mean content attains 1 percent, no appreciable decrease of content with depth being noticed. The greatest concentration of beryl is characteristic of albite pockets occurring within the small-block pegmatite at the boundary between the zone of medium-grained pegmatite and the zone of block microcline. A belt enriched in beryl is thus segregated, that extends along the boundary of the paragenetic complexes referred to above. The beryl-bearing zone extends along the hanging-wall, where it also has a greater thickness. In the recumbent side of the stock the zone has discontinuities and is characterized by a lesser thickness and a lower beryl concentration.

Table 19 | *Characteristic paragenesis of minerals of the stock-shaped bulge of spodumene-albite pegmatite (Fig. 22)*

ZONES	ROCK-FORMING MINERALS	ACCESSORY MINERALS	RARE-METAL MINERALS	MINOR MINERALS
Zone of graphic and medium-grained pegmatite of apographic structure.	Microcline, albite, quartz.	Muscovite.	—	—
Zone of pockets of saccharoidal albite.	Albite.	Muscovite, quartz, garnet.	Beryl, tantalite, lithiophilite.	Apatite, bismutite.
Zone of block microcline.	Microcline-perthite.	—	—	—
Quartz-muscovite zone.	Quartz, muscovite.	Garnet, tourmaline.	Beryl, bismuto-tantalite, tantalite.	Bismutite, apatite.
Spodumene-cleavelandite zone.	Cleavelandite, spodumene, quartz.	Muscovite.	Alkali-beryl, columbite, lithiophillite.	
Quartz-spodumene zone.	Quartz, spodumene.	Albite.	—	—
Zone of pockets of fine-lamellar albite.	Albite.	Lithiophillite.	Microlite, tantalite.	Apatite.
Zone of block quartz (with blocks of microcline-perthite).	Quartz, microcline-perthite.	—	Pollucite.	—
Lepidolite zone.	Lepidolite, albite.	—	Alkali-beryl, mangano-tantalite.	

The next beryl-bearing zone is the quartz-muscovite zone occurring as irregular pockets along the inner boundary of the block-microcline zone. The beryl of the quartz-muscovite replacement complex is characterized by greenish-blue color and well-developed crystal faces, the size of the crystals varying between 0.5×2 to 1.5×10 cm. The beryl distribution in the zone is relatively uniform. It is interesting to note that, as the depth increased by 30–40 m, the content of beryl in this zone decreased from 1 to 0.2 percent.

The white or rose alkali-lithium and lithium-caesium beryl is characteristic of the cleavelandite-spodumene zone of the stock, which is the beryl-spodumene ore-zone. The beryl crystals have a habit from short prismatic to tabular, with poorly developed faces. Individual crystals vary in size from two to several scores of centimeters across. The distribution of beryl is in pockets, and extremely irregular. Individual pockets in portions of the stock near the surface contained as much as 1 ton of beryl. The beryl content decreases with depth. The increased concentration of irregular crystals of water-clear rosterite is characteristic also of the lepidolite zone developed in the upper horizons of the stock-shaped bulge as a transgressing lens that overlaps the apical part of the quartz core of the stock.

Unlike the stock-shaped bulge, the gently-dipping part of the pegmatite is characterized by weak differentiation, and its major part is composed of medium-grained albitized pegmatite with disseminated beryl.

2. The Buckhorn deposit Larimer County, Colorado, U.S.A. (Cameron et al., 1951) is a zoned pegmatite dike of spodumene-albite composition. The dike is 180 m long (with a thickness of 10–12 m in the productive part) and lies conformably within micaceous schists. The central part of the dike is composed of a quartz-spodumene zone that contains cleavelandite (at the southwest end of the dike spodumene disappears, and the zone consists of pure quartz with cleavelandite). The axial zone of quartz-spodumene is surrounded by a beryl-containing quartz-muscovite-albite zone that is best developed in the north-eastern half of the dike.

The outer zone of the pegmatite is medium-grained albitized microcline-quartz pegmatite with muscovite.

The deposit has been mined both opencast and in depth from shafts.

3. The beryl-bearing lepidolite-albite pegmatites can be illustrated by the example of the complex tantalum-beryllium deposit at the Harding mine, Taos County, New Mexico, U.S.A. (Cameron et al., 1951). This deposit was mined for the purpose of extracting microlite, tantalite, and beryl, and is characterized by a high content of beryl, also of both tantalite and microlite.

The pegmatitic formations of the Harding deposit are genetically related to the so-called Dixon granites, and occur among amphibolites and micaceous schists of preCambrian age.

The most interesting pegmatitic bodies containing beryl and microlite occur in amphibolites. The main pegmatitic body is a flat lens 305 × 183 m with a thickness of 18 m.

The pegmatite has a zonal structure with a separate quartz core containing large crystals of albitized microcline-perthite and pockets of a lepidolite-albite aggregate.

The central core is surrounded by a zone consisting of spodumene, albite, and muscovite, with large pockets of the albite-lepidolite complex, which contain large quantities of disseminated brown-black microlite and tantalite. The outer pegmatite zone consists of a coarse-grained quartz-albite-muscovite aggregate with inclusions of large crystals of white beryl and of relics of albitized microcline-perthite.

Higher concentrations of the caesium-containing rose-colored beryl are also related to the quartz core of the pegmatite, where beryl is the essential component of the albite replacement complex which, in the massive quartz of the core, forms a series of stockworks controlled by fractures and consisting of cleavelandite, quartz, and rose beryl.

The interesting pegmatitic vein in Mora County, N. Mex., U.S.A. (Cameron et al., 1951) mined to a depth slightly exceeding 10 m, for lepidolite, beryl, and microlite, may be regarded as belonging to the replaced lepidolite-albite pegmatites. The vein extends for about 23 m, its thickness in the bulge is as much as 5 m. The pegmatitic body transgresses the fine-grained amphibole schist and is characterized by a well-pronounced zonality. A cleavelandite-lepidolite zone containing microlite and rose beryl of the vorobyevite type occurs around the quartz core and replaces the outer zone which is composed of medium- and coarse-grained pegmatite. In addition to beryl one finds in the vein slight quantities of gadolinite (yttrium and beryllium silicate).

Figures 21–23 show vertical sections and plans of the individual horizons of the characteristic pegmatitic deposits of the group under consideration, that

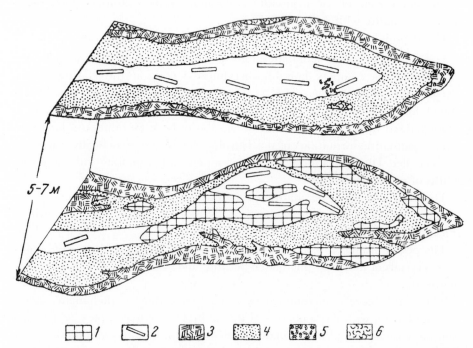

Fig. 23. Nature of the change along the dip of the replaced spodumene-albite pegmatite in a small, lens-shaped pegmatite. (1) Block microcline-perthite; (2) quartz-spodumene zone; (3) quartz-muscovite zone; (4) albite zone; (5) lepidolite replacement complex; (6) greisen replacement complex.

illustrate various cases of the zonal variation of the pegmatitic body with depth.

Figure 23 shows a relatively small lens-shaped pegmatite whose length is 78 m and in the bulge attains a thickness of 12 m. The pegmatite occurs in metamorphosed quartz-micaceous schists and is characterized by a distinct zonal structure. The central part of the bulge of the pegmatite consists of the quartz-spodumene zone containing rare crystals of vorobyevite and rosterite. The quartz-spodumene core is surrounded by a thick (as much as 5 m thickness) cleavelandite zone containing inclusions of white beryl, cassiterite, plates of columbite, spessartite, and pockets of altered lithiophilite. Along the pegmatite contact is a quartz-muscovite zone containing relics of albitized medium-grained pegmatite. Here also one finds the characteristic conical crystals of white alkali-beryl.

The zonality of the pegmatite varies fairly sharply with depth as is shown by a decrease in thickness at the expense of large blocks of microcline-perthite, which occur in the core. At a depth of 7 m from the surface the pegmatite already shows a transition to replaced muscovite-albite pegmatites.

Of somewhat different nature is the vertical zoning of the Hardesty-Homestead pegmatite Pennington County, S. Dakota, U.S.A. (Cameron et al., 1951), whose bulge, exposed at the surface, tapers off fairly sharply with depth (Fig. 24). The quartz core and the albitized quartz-spodumene zone with amblygonite, which surrounds the core, tapers along with the bulge. Only the

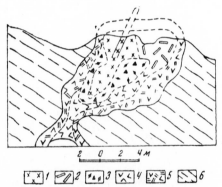

Fig. 24. Section through the Hardesty-Homestead pegmatite, showing the sharp zonal variation with depth, Pennington County, South Dakota (after Cameron et al., 1951). (1) Solid quartz (core); (2) microcline-perthite pegmatite; (3) amblygonite-spodumene pegmatite with tantalite; (4) quartz-albite pegmatite; (5) muscovite-quartz-albite pegmatite; (6) garnet-mica schists.

albite zone, which forms the central part of the vein here, and the quartz-albite-muscovite zone adjacent to the contact continue in depth. Down dip below the contraction is a bulge in which one should expect again a sharp zonal change.

As an example of vertical zoning of a pegmatite in which erosion has exposed only the apical part, one can refer to a typical pegmatitic vein that is very strongly albitized and greisenized. At one of the ends, it dips into a blind (apical) body. The vein lies in gabbro and is characterized by a varying dip that gives it a stepped shape. Its textural-paragenetic peculiarities make it a characteristic representative of replaced muscovite-albite pegmatites with beryl,

Plan of level I (exit to surface)

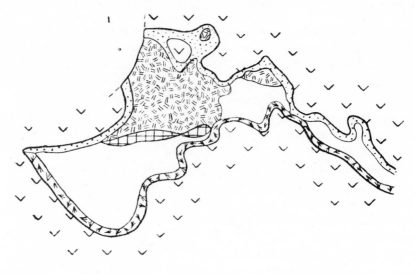

Plan of level 2 (40M along vein dip)

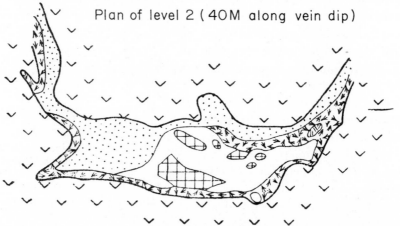

Plan of level 3 (65M along vein dip)

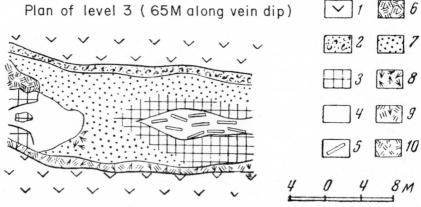

4 0 4 8 M

columbite, and microlite; a transition to replaced spodumene-albite pegmatites is noticeable in the bulge.

The zonality of the apical (blind) part of the pegmatite is characterized by the predominance of the greisen zone which, along with block quartz, fills the whole central part of the lens-shaped bulges of the vein (Fig. 25). At the hanging-wall and foot-wall the greisen zone is bordered by an albite zone which directly adjoins the contact with gabbro. The cleavelandite complex is segregated in the hanging-wall of the vein, whereas the foot-wall is composed of fine-grained albite separated by a thin cleavelandite fringe from the central zones. In attenuations of the pegmatite the central zones (greisen and block-quartz) usually die out, and the vein is wholly composed of the albite replacement complex (cleavelandite in the hanging-wall and fine-grained albite in the foot-wall). In bulges at the boundary between block quartz on the hanging-wall and the greisen fine-lamellar muscovite on the foot-wall there are irregular relict segregations of block microcline-perthite. In the apical part of the vein, beryl is present in fairly high concentrations (about 1 percent), as aggregates of large irregular crystals of white, rose, and greenish color at the boundary between the cleavelandite zone and inner zones (block-quartz and greisen) of the pegmatite. It occurs in smaller quantities in the greisen-albite replacement complex. Lithiophilite, apatite, columbite, microlite, and zircon occur in association with alkali-beryl.

At the depth of 40 m along the dip the greisen zone disappears almost completely, the central part of the bulge in this horizon being composed of the block-quartz zone which includes relatively large blocks as well as smaller idiomorphic crystals of microcline-perthite. The block-quartz zone is edged with a cleavelandite zone in which one finds, at the footwall, pocket-shaped rudimentary formations of the greisen replacement complex.

In the hanging-wall of the vein the cleavelandite zone which edges the quartz core directly adjoins the contact, whereas in the footwall there extends along the contact a zone of fine-grained saccharoidal albite, in which, as the depth increases, there begin to appear relics of medium-grained albitized pegmatite of apographic structure.

The zonal change which takes place at a depth of 65 m along the dip from

---

Fig. 25. Plans of the individual levels of a blind (apical) pegmatite vein with strongly developed replacement phenomena; these plans illustrate the transition with increasing depth of the greisen-albite pegmatite (first level) into muscovite-albite pegmatite (second level) and into a spodumene-albite horizon (third level). (1) Gabbro; (2) zone of the albitized medium-grained pegmatite of apographic structure; (3) block microcline; (4) block quartz; (5) quartz-spodumene zone; (6) muscovite replacement complex; (7) fine-grained albite replacement complex; (8) cleavelandite replacement complex; (9) muscovite with cleavelandite; (10) greisen replacement complex.

outcrop of the vein is very interesting. The general features of the zoning are as follows: a continuous zone of albitized medium-grained pegmatite of apographic structure extends along the contact of the foot-wall of the vein; the proportion of quartz and muscovite in the cleavelandite zone of the hanging-wall of the vein increases and marks the transition to a quartz-muscovite complex; cleavelandite, associated in upper horizons only with the hanging-wall of the pegmatite, occurs here in the form of small pockets containing relics of microcline among predominant saccharoidal albite; the number of quartz and microcline blocks and their dimensions markedly increases in the bulge (immediately below the surface part of the bulge which is composed of greisen zone) and spodumene appears in block pegmatite (the quartz-spodumene zone) and here the beryl content drops roughly to one-tenth.

THE GRANITIC PEGMATITES OF THE CROSSING-LINE. These differ considerably from ordinary pure pegmatites referred to above, being characterized by a number of specific geological and mineralogic-geochemical peculiarities. In a number of cases the vein bodies usually referred to the crossing-line group of pegmatites have an obvious similarity to hydrothermal-pneumatolytic deposits, owing to which some authors regard the crossing-line pegmatites as deposits basically related not to pegmatitic, but to pneumatolytic and hydrothermal processes.

The crossing-line pegmatite fields usually lie within the exo-contact zones of pegmatite-bearing granitic intrusions in various basic and ultra-basic rocks that are considerably altered by the processes of regional metamorphism. In the endo-contact belt of similar intrusions there usually develop streaky pegmatitic units which at places carry druses containing crystals of topaz and beryl.

The altered basic and ultrabasic rocks enclosing the pegmatites are usually represented by amphibole schists, amphibole diorites, and serpentinites which, in a number of places, are transformed to talc, chlorite, actinolite, or tremclite schists.

The beryl-bearing ore-bodies have a complex structure and consist of separate veins that alternately unite and diverge. The rows of such veins form a thick series (Fig. 26) which extend for hundreds of meters. Individual beryl-bearing veins in the series have a thickness of from 5 to 6 m and extend for a few scores of meters. The vein series can be traced to a considerable depth (Fig. 27).

The beryl-bearing vein bodies of the crossing-line are subdivided into the following fundamental groups on the basis of mineralogical composition and structure: (1) mica-plagioclase and mica veins with beryl, (2) beryl-muscovite-fluorite veins, and (3) beryl-muscovite-quartz veins.

Mica-plagioclase and mica veins with beryl are the most common among the beryl-bearing formations of the group under consideration. These types of veins

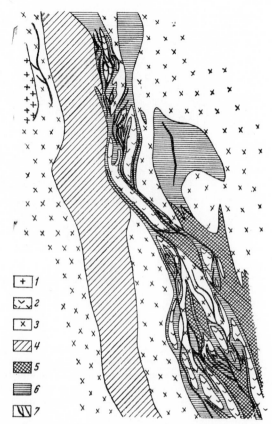

Fig. 26. Series of beryl-bearing mica-plagioclase veins transgressing ultrabasic rocks. (1) Two-mica granite; (2) serpentinites and talc-carbonate rocks; (3) amphibolite; (4) carbonaceous amphibole schist; (5) diorite porphyrite; (6) talc, chlorite, and actinolite rocks; (7) beryl-bearing micaceous-plagioclase veins.

were studied and described in detail quite a time ago by Fersman (1931, 1940) and later by Vlasov (1938); these authors clearly described the structure and paragenetic peculiarities of mica-plagioclase bodies which they referred to the category of desilicated pegmatites. The zonal structure is highly characteristic of beryl-bearing veins; however, it is not always shown with sufficient clearness. The central part of the veins consists entirely of coarse-grained plagioclase (plagioclasite) which forms individual discrete lenses (Fig. 28) and, less commonly, continuous, vein-shaped bodies as much as 1.5 m thick (Fig. 29). On either side of the plagioclase core there lie reaction zones: the phlogopite zone, as much as 6 m thick; the actinolite zone, much less thick (0.2–0.3 m), and developed intermittently in the form of separate lenses; the chlorite zone, as much as 2 m thick, and the talc zone which occurs in veins cutting serpentinites. In

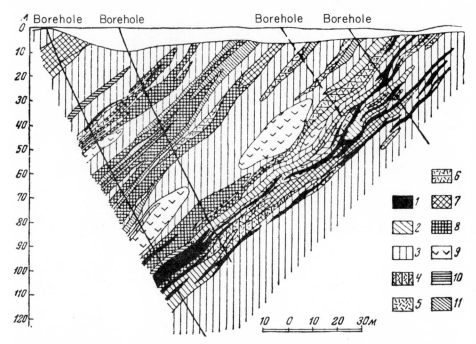

Fig. 27. Section through the series of beryl-bearing micaceous-plagioclase veins. (1) Phlogopite with plagioclase cores; (2) phlogopite-talc, phlogopite-actinolite, and phlogopite-chlorite schists; (3) talc schists; (4) talc-actinolite schists; (5) actinolite schists; (6) actinolite-chlorite schists; (7) diorites; (8) amphibolites; (9) serpentinites; (10) chlorite schists; (11) carbonaceous schists.

a number of places the actinolite and chlorite zones are absent, in which case the talc zone follows immediately after the phlogopite zone. In individual veins the plagioclasite cores have only small dimensions, and the vein is mainly composed of a solid phlogopite.

Besides the medium plagioclase and phlogopite, the characteristic minerals of the mica-plagioclase and mica veins are: beryl, phenacite, chrysoberyl, margarite, tourmaline, prochlorite, bavenite, gilbertite, fuchsite, molybdenite, chlorite, talc, and apatite.

The main mass of beryl, and of the rarer emerald which, however, is characteristic of such deposits, is associated with the phlogopite-rock (Fig. 30); a smaller quantity of these minerals is included in the plagioclase cores, whereas only single crystals occur in the chlorite zone.

The crystals are usually well-developed. Their color varies from yellow-green and green in the case of common beryl to light-green for emerald. Along with large crystals, from 10 to 30 cm along the c-axis, one finds a great many crystals less than 0.5 × 1 cm.

Phenacite is usually related to the chlorite zone of the reaction complex or

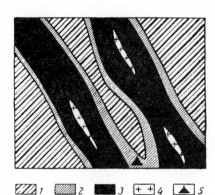

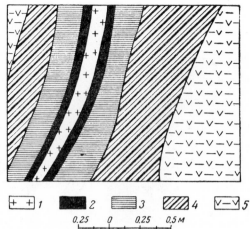

Fig. 28. Lenses of plagioclasite in fine-lamellar phlogopite (according to Vlasov, 1938). (1) Talc-dolomite rock; (2) chlorite; (3) phlogopite; (4) plagioclasite; (5) chrysoberyl.

Fig. 29. Vein-shaped plagioclasite body with symmetric reaction zones of phlogopite and quartz (according to Vlasov, 1938). (1) Plagioclasite; (2) phlogopite; (3) talc; (4) talc-dolomite rock; (5) metamorphozed dunite.

else it occurs at the contact between the chlorite and phlogopite zone. Its crystals are, as a rule, colorless; less frequently they are wine-yellow with dimension in cross section of from 1 to 10 cm.

Chrysoberyl is, like phenacite, associated with the chlorite zone; it occurs less often in the phlogopite zone and in the plagioclasite core. It is characterized by green and yellow-green lamellar crystals that frequently form characteristic trillings.

The size of the crystals varies from 0.5 to 6 cm in cross section. It should be noted that, quantitatively, phenacite and chrysoberyl are much less abundant than beryl and in the deposits of the group studied they account for an insignificant part of the total beryllium combined in beryllium minerals.

The beryl-muscovite-fluorite veins usually occur in massive

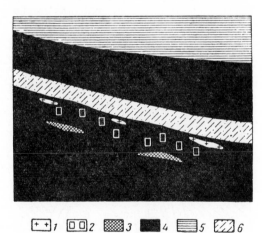

Fig. 30. Beryl in phlogopite (according to Vlasov, 1938). (1) Plagioclasite; (2) beryl; (3) actinolite; (4) phlogopite; (5) talc; (6) metamorphozed diorite.

basic rocks of the diorite type; in composition, they are typical representatives of hydrothermal-pneumatolytic formations (Fig. 31). The main minerals of

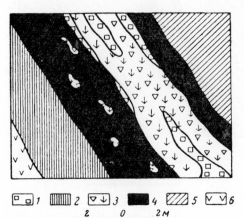

vein formations of this group are: beryl (50–60 percent of the vein mass) and fluorite (25–30 percent). Less important are muscovite and plagioclase. Very small quantities of fluorapatite, prochlorite, molybdenite, and native bismuth are found. The veins are from 1–2 to 5 m thick and are traced in length and dip for 100 to 120 m.

Fig. 31. Beryl-muscovite-fluorite vein in ultrabasic rocks (according to Vlasov, 1938). (1) Fluorite; (2) talc schist; (3) beryl and muscovite; (4) mica; (5) diorite; (6) serpentine.

The beryl-muscovite-quartz veins (Fig. 32) commonly found in the fields of crossing-line pegmatites as a rule, can be related also to the category of hydrothermal-pneumatolytic formations. These veins are composed of quartz (as much as 90 percent) and muscovite and albite are of much lesser significance in their composition. Individual bodies have this zonal structure: an albite zone (8 to 10 cm) at the contacts, next a muscovite zone with a small content of beryl, molybdenite, and chalcopyrite. Then a muscovite-beryl zone that con-

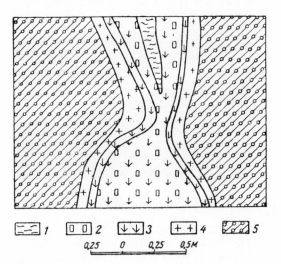

Fig. 32. Beryl-muscovite-quartz vein in diorite (according to Vlasov, 1938). (1) Quartz; (2) beryl; (3) muscovite; (4) plagioclasite; (5) dioritic porphyrite.

sists of light-blue beryl and muscovite 10 to 12 cm in thickness and forms the edge of the thickest and most central zone composed of quartz. It should be noted that, in the narrower parts, the veins usually consist of a muscovite-beryl aggregate. Besides quartz, muscovite, and beryl, the veins of this group contain insignificant quantities of fluorite, molybdenite, and copper sulfides.

Hydrothermal-pneumatolytic Beryllium Deposits

Beryllium-bearing Greisens and Related Veins

Beryllium deposits of hydrothermal-pneumatolytic origin are closely related to the greisen and vein deposits of wolframite-quartz and cassiterite-quartz as well as to skarn deposits enriched in fluorite and magnetite. They contain, in a number of places, increased concentrations of tungsten, tin, and molybdenum. The overwhelming majority of hydrothermal-pneumatolytic beryllium deposits are complex beryl-wolframite or beryl-cassiterite deposits (Table 20).

All similar deposits are found in the areas of acid and ultra-acid granites of medium depth; at the same time the greisen and quartz-vein beryllium deposits show a preferential relationship to the so-called small intrusions whose granites are transformed to a greater or lesser extent by postmagmatic processes (mainly greisenization).

The greisen beryllium deposits are usually represented by the tungsten-, tin-, and molybdenum-bearing greisen bodies containing disseminated beryl, in many places associated with bertrandite. It should be noted that the size and nature of beryllium segregations place the greisen formations, in an overwhelming majority of cases, in the category of beryllium deposits whose utilization requires the application of mechanical methods of beneficiation.

The morphological features of beryl-bearing greisens are determined by the nature of fracturing which was utilized by the ore-bearing emanations and solutions that caused the greisenization of the enclosing granites or of rocks of kindred composition. In this case the fractures which control the deposits of this group are mainly fine contraction fractures formed during the process of solidification of the parent intrusion. The nature of such fractures governs the predominant development of stockwork bodies which are highly characteristic of greisen deposits.

By classifying the greisen formations into greisens proper and greisens forming edges of the vein segregations of quartz, F. I. Vol'fson (1954) distinguishes three main structural types of greisen deposits proper:

1. stockworks in granites at intersections of contiguous contractional fractures in two directions (they are characterized by a considerable surface area of development and small depth);

2. stockwork zones associated with contractional fractures of predominantly

Table 20 | *Main paragenetic associations of vein type hydrothermal-pneumatolytic beryllium deposits*

TYPE OF VEIN-FILLING	MAIN MINERALS	ORE-MINERALS (COMMON)	ACCESSORY VEIN MINERALS	ACCESSORY ORE-MINERALS
Quartz-feldspar.	Quartz, feldspar.	Wolframite, beryl.	Muscovite, topaz, fluorite.	Scheelite, sulfides.
Hematite-quartz-feldspar, hematite-quartz.	Do.	Hematite, wolframite, helvite-danalite, beryl.	Biotite, topaz, fluorite.	Scheelite, sulfides, magnetite.
Wolframite-quartz, and beryl-wolframite-quartz.	Quartz.	Wolframite, beryl.	Potassium feldspar, topaz, fluorite, muscovite.	Cassiterite, molybdenite, bismutite, helvite, pyrite, chalcopyrite.
Molybdenite-quartz.	Do.	Molybdenite, beryl.	Muscovite, topaz, fluorite.	Cassiterite, wolframite bismuth, bismutite, sulfides.
Scheelite-quartz.	Do.	Scheelite.	Fluorite.	Beryl, bismuth, pyrite.
Topaz-quartz.	Quartz, topaz.	Wolframite, beryl.	Muscovite, fluorite.	Cassiterite, rutile.
Muscovite-quartz.	Quartz, muscovite.	Beryl.	Fluorite, topaz, bertrandite.	Woframite, molybdenite.
Beryl-muscovite.	Muscovite, beryl.	Beryl.	Quartz, fluorite, topaz, tourmaline, bertrandite.	Wolframite.
Fluorite-biotite.	Biotite, fluorite.	Beryl.	Oligoclase, orthoclase, sericite.	Pyrite.

one direction (compared with the former type they are characterized by a smaller surface area of development, but a greater depth);

3. ore-bearing greisens in conjugated steeply-dipping and gently-dipping fractures.

F. I. Vol'fson (1954) discriminates stockworks in granites under a slightly permeable cover of roof rocks as a separate characteristic type.

The greisen formations which accompany the vein segregations of quartz are characterized by somewhat different morphological features that will be dealt with below in the description of beryllium deposits related to feldspar-quartz and quartz veins.

On the basis of mineralogical composition, the beryl-bearing greisens can be subdivided into quartz-mica, mica, quartz, quartz-topaz, and quartz-hematite varieties. One should note here the close morphological and paragenetic features in most of the types listed. The most common are the quartz-mica greisens.

One of the typical deposits of this group is at the contact between the granite mass of Variscan age and the Caledonian gneissic granites that break through the metamorphosed rocks composed of phyllite, schists, quartzites, and porphyrites of preCambrian age. The greisen bodies are localized in a narrow zone, 20 to 60 m thick and as much as 1000 to 1500 m long, and have the form of steeply-dipping lenses whose length varies from 5–7 to 400 m, and whose thickness varies from 2–5 cm to 10 m. They are subdivided, on the basis of their composition, into quartz-mica, mica, and quartz greisens. The characteristic minerals of the greisens are quartz, feldspar, muscovite, fluorite, beryl, wolframite, hematite, magnetite, and more rarely cassiterite, molybdenite, zircon, topaz, monazite, and some sulfides. Higher concentrations of beryl are associated with quartz-mica and mica greisens. In quartz-mica greisens beryl forms small pockets and lenses from 3 × 3 to 5 × 15 cm, highly irregularly distributed. Besides being in pocket-shaped accumulations, beryl also is present as monomineralic streaks 1 to 1.5 cm thick, which are as much as 5 m long. Such streaks are especially characteristic of the micaceous varieties of greisen where they occur in the central portions of mica segregations. In addition to beryl, wolframite is found in commercial quantities in greisens.

An example of the fairly rare greisen deposits with a helvite mineralization is a deposit that lies in the endo-contact zone of the coarse, granular porphyritic granite mass which intrudes the volcanic rocks of Lower Devonian system.

The greisen bodies, separated by 150 to 200 m, extend for as much as 150 m; they attain a thickness of 20 m, and they form gently dipping structures controlled by the contraction cracks of the granites. On the basis of the mineralogical composition, they are quartz-mica-hematite and mica-quartz greisens. The former contain helvite, whereas the latter are characterized by higher beryl concentrations. The helvite-bearing greisen bodies have a characteristic zonal structure: the outer part of the greisen body is composed of quartz-mica greisen 15 to 20 cm thick, which is followed by quartz-hematite greisen among which one observes accumulations of almost pure hematite and pocket-shaped segregations of helvite. Besides helvite there is sparsely disseminated danalite and bertrandite in the greisen. Fluorite, garnet, and opal may be accessory greisen minerals. Tourmaline and magnetite are rarer. Helvite is distributed non-uniformly in the greisen body; in some portions its content attains 60 to

80 percent, whereas in other portions it is almost absent. Bertrandite is found
as very small lamellae and radially fibrous aggregates which form at the expense
of helvite.

A beryllium deposit in feldspar-quartz and quartz veins has many features in
common with the greisen deposits proper, referred to above. Many vein deposits
of this group are associated en échelon with greisens which contain beryllium
minerals.

The structural features of beryllium deposits in feldspar-quartz and quartz
veins which, in accordance with F. I. Vol'fson's (1954) classification, enables
the following basic types to be distinguished among them:

1. veins in contraction cracks among granitoids;
2. steeply dipping veins in fault fractures;
3. veins in tectonic shear zones.

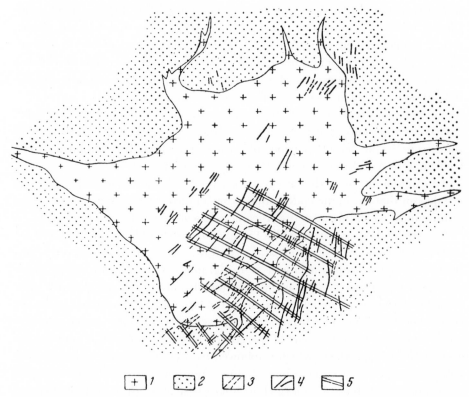

Fig. 33. Quartz and quartz-feldspar veins with wolframite and beryl in tear faults.
(1) Porphyritic muscovite granites; (2) sandstones showing alteration to hornfels,
and quartz-feldspar hornfels; (3) quartz-feldspar veins and streaks; (4) quartz
veins and streaks; (5) prospecting trenches.

The first type of vein formation, those related to contraction cracks, is usually represented by relatively thin streaks rapidly thinning out in depth and forming in a number of cases typical stockwork zones. In individual deposits the beryl concentration in the streaks is fairly high, although the overall dimensions of deposits are usually not large.

Steeply-dipping veins in fault fractures present a very common structural type in the fields of beryl-wolframite-quartz deposits. Handicapped from the commercial viewpoint by a limited extension in length and depth, they form extensive ore fields which contain a large number of vein formations (Fig. 33); in a number of places, this enables deposits of this type to be profitably worked for rare metals.

The third type of vein formation associated with shear zones and accompanied by greisens is characterized by the greatest constancy as regards extension and dip. There are vein bodies in shear fractures, which extend for 1000 m and more. From the commercial viewpoint this structural type is the most promising (fig. 34).

The paragenetic features of beryllium deposits in feldspar-quartz and quartz veins are highly characteristic and are characterized by the dominance

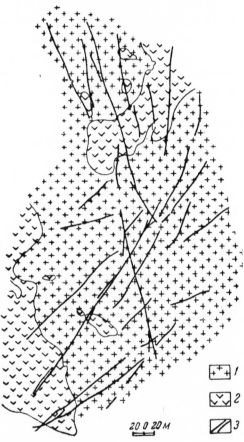

20 0 20 M

Fig. 34. Beryl-bearing quartz veins in shear fractures. (1) Granite; (2) quartz porphyries and tuffs; (3) quartz veins with beryl and wolframite.

of potassium feldspar, muscovite, fluorite, topaz, and beryl. The relative abundance of these minerals varies from one deposit to another, which makes it possible to outline the basic paragenetic groups of beryllium deposits related to hydrothermal-pneumatolytic vein formations (Table 20).

The commonest of the listed paragenetic types of beryl-bearing veins are the quartz-feldspar and quartz type with beryl and wolframite, also the quartz type with beryl and molybdenite. High beryllium concentrations are also noted in the rarer topaz-quartz and beryl-muscovite vein formations.

Several characteristic examples are considered. One of the typical deposits of the wolframite-quartz group is related to a large stockwork of late-Variscan granites that intrude the volcanic rocks of Lower and Middle Devonian. The granites of the stock are broken by a series of north-easterly shear fractures that control numerous ore veins developed within the stock and in its exo-contact zone. On the basis of the mineralogical features, the ore veins can be divided into the feldspar-quartz, molybdenite-quartz, and wolframite-quartz varieties which contain beryl and helvite.

The vein segregations, consisting essentially of quartz, are accompanied by greisen fringes of a mica-quartz and mica-quartz-topaz composition. The extension of the largest veins is 1500 m and thickness is 1.5 m. Among the common minerals of the most interesting wolframite-quartz-beryl-bearing veins are beryl, wolframite, helvite, potassium feldspar, cassiterite, molybdenite, muscovite, sericite, pyrite, topaz, and fluorite. Less common are bertrandite, bismutite, arsenopyrite, carbonates, etc.

Beryl occurs usually in the greisen fringes and in the central portions of quartz veins, forming druses as much as 5 to 10 cm across consisting of an aggregate of beryl crystals with dimensions from 0.3×3 to 0.5×1 cm.

Helvite in the form of aggregates of small greenish and yellowish-brown crystals is found scattered in the vein quartz along with aggregates of sulfides. Bertrandite which forms when helvite is replaced by carbonates (siderite and rhodochrosite) occurs in close association with helvite. Wolframite is in economic concentrations in the deposits.

Another beryl-wolframite deposit, characterized by the absence of greisen fringes along the contacts of quartz veins, is related to a mass of two-mica porphyritic granite broken by a system of north-westerly shear fractures. The quartz veins which fill the shear fractures are traced for as much as 500 m; the thickness of various veins varies from 4 to 65 cm. Finely-crystalline beryl is obtained in various proportions in all veins, whereas wolframite only in some veins. It is characteristic that thin veins and apophyses of veins have a higher beryl concentration (Fig. 35); in veins 4 to 5 cm thick, it is 75–80 percent of the vein mass.

Besides widespread beryl, and the rarer wolframite, one finds feldspar, fluorite, scheelite, arsenopyrite, pyrite, and scorodite in quartz veins. Next to quartz, beryl is the most widespread mineral; it occurs as crystals with well-developed faces and as continuous granular masses which form characteristic fringes along the selvages of the vein. The color of beryl varies from greenish-yellow and bright yellow to colorless. Crystal dimensions usually do not exceed 3 to 4×0.3 to 0.5 cm, attaining in some cases 2×10 cm. In view of these crystal sizes it is necessary to apply mechanical methods of beneficiation for the extraction of beryl.

Still another type of deposit with complexly-shaped ore bodies occurs in the zone of endo- and exo-contact of granite porphyries with "hornfelsed" and greisenized aleurolites, phyllites, and sandstones of Palaeozoic age. The most interesting beryl-bearing body is a complex stockwork formed by a network of streaks and metasomatic bodies characterized by different stages of mineralizsation. Within the deposit E. I. Dolomanova distinguishes among the following types of streak segregations: (1) beryl-topaz-quartz; (2) beryl-feldspar; (3) cassiterite-muscovite-topaz; (4) tourmaline-fluorite-sulfide; (5) fluorite-albite; (6) quartz-fluorite-chlorite.

The mineralogical composition of the streaks: quartz, topaz, tourmaline, beryl, biotite, albite, muscovite, microcline-perthite, fluorite, wolframite, arsenopyrite, rutile, zircon, cassiterite, monazite, apatite, spinel, corundum, scheelite, epidote, ilmenite, pyrite, bismutite, tetradymite, joseite, native bismuth, molybdenite, gold, sphalerite, stannite, chalcopyrite, chlorite, siderite, calcite, bertrandite, hydromuscovite, hematite, and a number of supergene minerals.

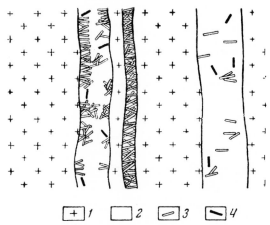

Fig. 35. Beryl and wolframite in quartz veins which transgress granite. The concentration of beryl in thin veins is noticeable. (1) Granite; (2) quartz; (3) beryl; (4) wolframite.

Beryl is characteristic of beryl-topaz-quartz, beryl-feldspar, and cassiterite-muscovite-topaz streaks (sig.). The beryl-topaz-quartz streaks branch out directly from the granite-porphyry streaks; the transition from granite porphyry to beryl-bearing quartz streaks with topaz and other minerals occurs gradually but within a small space. Beryl forms long-prismatic crystals 3 to 4 mm across. Radiating aggregates of crystals are observed in the selvages of the streaks or in their central part. The beryl-feldspar streaks which consist of variable amounts of feldspar, quartz, and beryl occur in greisenized granite porphyry and in greisen bodies composed of muscovite and quartz.

Beryl predominates in the streaks in the greisen, and sometimes is the only component of individual streak sections. Fluorite and wolframite are in association with beryl.

Quartz-vein formations with helvite-danalite mineralization have a very characteristic paragenesis. The geological features of such deposits are similar to those of the normal beryl-containing wolframite-quartz deposits referred to above. At the same time the deposits of this group differ in geochemical respect from the other deposits by high concentrations of iron, zinc, and sulfur. In this connection hematite and some sulfides are the typomorphic minerals of quartz and feldspar-quartz veins containing helvite and danalite. Vein formations are often accompanied by hematite-quartz greisens which likewise contain helvite and danalite.

A deposit which occurs in the endo-contact zone of a not very large intrusive mass composed of coarse- and medium-grained biotite granites can be used as an example. The granitites intrude a mass of volcanic rocks of Middle Devonian age. Quartz veins which fill the cracks in the granites are traced for as much as 450 m; their thickness varying from 1 to 50 m. The veins are accompanied by mica-quartz and hematite-quartz greisen fringes. The widespread minerals in quartz veins are: feldspar, hematite, biotite, danalite, helvite, beryl, topaz, fluorite, muscovite, wolframite, garnet, and bertrandite; quite common also are the sulfides of iron, copper, and zinc; monazite, allanite, zircon, rutile, sphene, and native bismuth are encountered less frequently. The helvite mineralization in the vein is usually pocket-shaped, the individual pocket aggregations of helvite attaining 20 cm across. Helvite is brown or yellowish, and its largest crystals are as much as 6 cm across. Disseminated small helvite crystals are also observed in the greisen around the vein.

It should be noted in conclusion that a late helvite mineralization is observed in individual cases in the vein quartz of polymetallic deposits. In such deposits helvite forms thin-crystalline aggregates of yellowish-green color, which segregate in the fissures of quartz and of other earlier minerals. Helvite and danalite are also found in small quantities in some vein deposits of the wolframite-quartz group, which occur in limestones.

The beryl-bearing fluorite pneumatolytes and hydrothermalites in limestones are genetically analogous to the greisen deposits of beryllium, which were formed in essentially different geological conditions among limestone masses. The fluorite bodies which contain beryllium minerals are usually large deposits of vein-type or more complex form; they occur in limestones at some distance from the beryllium-bearing granite intrusion (hundreds of meters). There are a number of common, characteristic features between this group of beryl-bearing formations and the skarn-type beryllium deposits (see below); however, the geological situation and the peculiarities of mineralogical composition point to the expediency of considering such deposits as belonging to a separate type.

The mineralogical composition of these beryllium-bearing formations is characterized by the predominance of fluorite; besides fluorite there is quartz, tourmaline, muscovite, and epidote. A valuable ore mineral may be cassiterite; less frequently wolframite. Beryllium minerals, finely disseminated and more concentrated in thin streaks within the fluorite, are represented by phenacite and chrysoberyl. A characteristic feature of these minerals is their insignificant size, from fractions of one millimeter to 1 to 2 mm, rarely more.

Interesting tin-fluorite deposits with beryllium minerals are found in the Seward peninsula (Alaska), but no data are available regarding the economic importance of these deposits.

Beryllium-bearing Skarn

The skarn-type beryllium deposits, related to the contact-metasomatic formations at the contact between beryllium-bearing granites and limestones, occur fairly widely and are known in various parts of the globe. At the same time there is apparent a well-defined relationship between the skarn-type beryllium deposits and the tungsten- or tin-bearing instrusive complexes which contain higher concentrations of fluorine. Such a relationship is shown in the normal occurrence of the beryllium-containing skarns within the tungsten-ore or tin-ore provinces as well as in the concomitant occurrence of beryllium with tungsten or tin in some skarn deposits enriched in fluorine.

The analysis of data available in the literature makes it possible to outline a number of characteristic textural and paragenetic features of the beryllium-bearing skarns.

Paragenetic Features

In an overwhelming majority of known deposits, fluorite and magnetite are the most characteristic rock-forming minerals of the beryllium-bearing skarns. The presence of insignificant quantities of beryllium minerals, however, also is noted in other types of skarns which contain fluorite and magnetite only as accessory components of the mineral complex.

The following types of beryllium-bearing skarns can be discriminated on the basis of the peculiarities of mineralogical composition:

1. Substantially magnetite skarns: fluorite-magnetite, mica-magnetite, fluorite-mica-magnetite, vesuvianite-magnetite, fluorite-vesuvianite-magnetite, pyroxene-vesuvianite-magnetite, and fluorite-feldspar-magnetite.

2. Substantially fluorite skarns: magnetite-fluorite, mica-fluorite, and mica-epidote-fluorite.

3. Other rarer skarns: epidote-garnet, fluorite-garnet, fluorite-feldspar, vesuvianite, and pyroxene.

Helvite, danalite, chrysoberyl, and phenacite are the most characteristic among the beryllium minerals proper, which become concentrated in the skarns.

Beryl and some other beryllium minerals were encountered in single cases in such deposits. A distinguishing feature of the beryllium skarn minerals is their fine-grained form which, as a rule, makes it very difficult to identify them without the application of optical and, especially, microchemical methods.

It has already been mentioned in the geochemical outline that skarn formations are characterized by the accumulation of beryllium as an isomorphous contamination in a number of the common skarn minerals (vesuvianite micas, etc.). The main "collector" of the dispersed beryllium in the deposits of the group under consideration appears to be vesuvianite which often contains about 1 percent or more of beryllium oxide.

Peculiarities of Texture

The most characteristic textural feature of the beryllium-bearing skarns is their thinly banded structure caused by the lamellar arrangement of the main rock-forming minerals: magnetite, on the one hand, and fluorite with associated silicates, on the other. The lamellae are layers enriched in magnetite; they are black, unlike the intermediate lighter-colored layers which are composed of fluorite and silicate minerals. The layers are usually wavy, and here and there corrugated, which imparts to the rock an extremely characteristic thinly-banded texture. The beryllium minerals usually concentrate in the light-colored streaks, but very small inclusions of these minerals are found, in a number of places also in magnetite.

The Iron Mountain deposit, New Mexico, U.S.A. (Jahns, 1944) is a typical example of beryllium-bearing skarn formations. The deposit consists of a thick series of limestones of the Magdalenian series, intersected in a complicated way by necks, sheets, and dikes of rhyolite, porphyritic rhyolite, and aplitic granite, presumably of Miocene age. The limestones which enclose the intrusive rocks are variably metamorphosed, and are "skarnized" near the contacts with the bodies of magmatic rocks.

The skarns consist essentially of magnetite, fluorite-magnetite, fluorite-mica-magnetite, and fluorite-vesuvianite-magnetite assemblages which, on the basis of texture and mineralogical composition, are sharply divided into two groups. The first group, characterized by massive texture, is represented by magnetite proper and garnet-magnetite skarns which contain a small proportion of fluorite (as much as 4 percent).

No beryllium minerals have been found in this group of skarn formation. The second group of skarns, which incorporates varieties richer in fluorite, is characterized by a typically lamellar (layer-like) texture, and contains higher concentrations of helvite and danalite. When the lamellar and the massive varieties of skarns occur side by side, the latter displays a tendency to be positioned between the lamellar skarn and the nearest contact of the intrusive body. The helvite-bearing skarns of the Iron Mountain usually consist of continuous (finely corrugated) lamellae 0.05 to 3 mm thick, each layer differing mineralogically from the adjacent layers. From the mineralogical viewpoint, the lamellar skarns are divided into the following varieties characterized by different helvite and danalite contents:

SKARN	HELVITE AND DANALITE CONTENT IN PERCENT
Fluorite-magnetite	2–24
Fluorite-mica-magnetite	traces-3
Fluorite-vesuvianite-magnetite	traces-1

The mineralogical composition (in percent) of the beryl-bearing skarn formations of the Iron Mountain deposit is given below.

	FLUORITE-MAGNETITE SKARN	FLUORITE-MICA-MAGNETITE AND FLUORITE-VESUVIANITE MAGNETITE SKARN
Magnetite	28–68	23–82
Fluorite	16–36	5–33
Helvite	2–24	traces-3
Vesuvianite	0	0–37
Biotite and chlorite	0–4	4–28
Adularia	0–9	0–2
Quartz	0–4	0–4
Alteration products (limonite, kaolinite etc.)	2–11	2–17
Garnet	0	0–7
Hematite	0	traces-7
Diopside	0	0–1
Clinozoisite	0	0–2
Sulphides	0	0-traces

PART II | Prospecting for and
Evaluating Beryllium
Deposits

Prospecting for Beryllium Deposits

The study of problems related to the methods of exploration and evaluation of beryllium deposits began relatively recently. Specific exploration procedures can be defined at present for the pegmatitic deposits which have been, until quite recently, the only commercial beryllium source in the world. However, as regards other types of beryllium deposits the possibility of their practical utilization is being studied at present, but the available data are so scarce that only a few conclusions can be drawn. These will require confirmation and further studies.

The prospection and subsequent utilization of beryllium deposits is divided, in general, into several successive stages:

1. choice of prospection area;

2. regional prospection for the purpose of area evaluation and detection of pegmatitic, greisen, or skarn fields;

3. prospection for promising beryl-bearing bodies within the limits of a pegmatitic, greisen, or skarn field;

4. detailed exploration and evaluation of yields for the purpose of detecting the most promising ore-bearing bodies;

5. commercial evaluation of beryllium deposits.

The description of successive operational stages as they pertain to pegmatitic and non-pegmatitic beryllium deposits is given below.

Choice of Area for the Organization of Small-scale Prospecting Work

The organization of small-scale beryllium prospection work should start with the collection of data relating to the geology, petrography, and "metallogenesis" of the area where it is intended to carry out prospecting work. When collecting these data one should strive to obtain the following information:

1. the nature of development of granitic intrusion complexes within the area, the composition of granites, the shape and geological situation of intrusive bodies, and the nature of rocks that enclose the granite intrusions;

2. the presence of pegmatitic, greisen, and skarn deposits and their composition;

3. the presence of other endogenous deposits in the area;

4. the results of sampling.

When no information whatever is available as regards the metal-bearing properties and when the area includes pegmatitic deposits, the choice of an area for the organization of small-scale prospecting work on pegmatites can be determined only by general geological features of the beryl-bearing pegmatitic fields, i.e. by their preferential relationship to the areas of development of large intrusions of medium depth, composed mainly of medium-grained biotite-microcline or porphyritic granites.

The structural analysis of the beryl-bearing pegmatitic fields shows that the enclosing rocks of such intrusions are, in an overwhelming majority of cases, psammitic deposits usually highly altered as a result of regional and contact metamorphism. In this connection it should be noted that a wide development of carbonate rocks in the endo-contact zone of the granite intrusion is a negative characteristic when selecting the area for instituting prospection for beryl-bearing pegmatites; at the same time one should however take into account and estimate the possibility of detecting other types of beryllium deposits, e.g. the beryllium-containing skarns, etc.

In the choice of the area for prospection the age of enclosing rocks and the age of the intrusion cannot be used as an exploration criterion. In different parts of the globe, the pegmatitic beryllium deposits are related both to the pre-Cambrian and Caledonian intrusions, and to the younger intrusions of the Hercynian, and even the early Cymmerian cycle.

The problem of selecting the area for instituting small-scale beryllium prospecting work is facilitated when one has at one's disposal information, however fragmentary, regarding the metal-bearing properties of the intrusive complexes and regarding the development of pegmatitic deposits within the area in question. The particulars relating to the following properties can be used as positive criteria:

1. the presence in the samples of at least one of the following minerals: beryl, tantalite, columbite, cassiterite (the latter to a lesser extent, because it may be related to other types of deposits);

2. the presence of pegmatitic deposits;

3. the occurrence of lithium or tantalum-niobium minerals and especially of beryl in outcrops or screes occurring at the place of origin.

As unfavorable criteria in this case one can consider information regarding a wide development, in the area, of greisen or hydrothermal deposits which do not usually associate spatially with pegmatitic fields.

At the same time the most general positive criterion for the choice of the area in which prospection for hydrothermal-pneumatolytic and contact-metasomatic beryllium deposits is to be carried out is the presence of greisen, quartz-vein, or skarn deposits of tungsten, tin, or molybdenum (see part I). When data relating to such deposits are not available in little-known areas, the analysis of the results of a sampling survey can be of considerable use. A very favorable criterion that enables the exploration work to be rationally carried out in any given case is the presence of the following minerals in samples: from the gangue—topaz, fluorite, and vesuvianite; from the ore—wolframite, cassiterite, molybdenite, and bismuth. When determining the area of prospection for the skarn beryllium deposits it is very desirable to carry out a spectroscopic investigation of museum specimens of vesuvianite for the presence of beryllium.

Tasks in the Small-scale (1/100,000–1/200,000) Prospecting for Beryl-bearing Pegmatites

The method of the small-scale prospecting work for beryl in pegmatites is determined in the first place by the geological features of the beryl-bearing pegmatitic fields, and partly by their structure and relationship to the parent granitic intrusions.

If no geological map of the corresponding scale is available for the prospection area, the prospecting work is complicated by the preparation of this map; as a matter of fact, prospection is carried out simultaneously with the geological survey.

The first task in the small-scale prospection consists of the mapping of the boundaries of the pegmatite-bearing area, and in marking out, in the area studied, the plots with the highest concentration of pegmatites.

It has been already mentioned in the first part of this publication that the regional structure of the rare-metal pegmatitic fields is determined, as a rule, by the morphological features and by the level of erosional exposure of the pegmatite-bearing parent intrusion.

A. I. Ginzburg (1949) who studied the prospection criteria of the rare-metal pegmatites, indicates the following main regularities of the layout of pegmatitic fields, related to the morphology of the intrusive body.

1. The pegmatitic fields extend for tens of kilometers, conformably with the trend of the basic structural lines of the area.

2. The zones of the endo- and exo-contact of the apical sections of the intrusion are the most favorable for the concentration of pegmatites. Then the trend of the pegmatitic fields is usually conformable with that of the contact line of the intrusion body, and changes in accordance with the latter.

3. In a number of cases the characteristic features are: the asymmetric relationship of pegmatitic fields to the granite intrusion and the preferential relationship of pegmatites to gently-dipping contacts of the intrusive bodies.

4. A relationship is noted between the pegmatitic fields and the sections in which a change occurs in the trend of the principal structural lines of the area, viz. the fold-axes, the axes of tectonic zones, and the axes of intrusion masses.

The relationship between the structure of pegmatitic fields and the nature of the erosional exposure of the granite intrusion, referred to in the first part of this publication, is shown in Table 21 prepared by A. I. Ginzburg (1949).

The determination of the peculiarities of the erosional exposure of the intrusion and the disclosure of the regularities in the distribution of pegmatitic fields is one of the major tasks in the small-scale prospection for beryl-bearing pegmatites.

Thus, the specific tasks in small-scale prospecting for the beryl-bearing pegmatites are reduced to the following:

1. The mapping of the boundaries of the pegmatitic area.

2. The mapping of the boundaries of the granite masses within the limits of the area, and the study of the dips of contacts of each intrusion.

3. Disclosure of tectonic zones within the limits of the granitic mass and of its endo-contact zone, as well as of the folding structure of the rocks of the intrusion roof.

4. Disclosure of large roof-pendants and of places where hybrid rocks developed within the limits of the granite intrusion.

5. Investigation of regularities in the distribution of pegmatitic fields in relation to the peculiarities of morphology and to the nature of erosional exposure of the granite intrusion.

Table 21	*Dependence of the disposition of pegmatitic fields on the nature of the erosional exposure of the intrusion*

STAGES OF EROSIONAL EXPOSURE	DISPOSITION OF PEGMATITIC FIELDS	SPECIALLY FAVORABLE SITES FOR THE CONCENTRATION OF THE RARE-METAL DEPOSITS
Superficial erosional exposure.	The pegmatitic fields are disposed far from the parent granites, commonly along the extension of large intrusions, above blind domes, around stocks and domes, and most frequently in the exo-contact zone, less frequently in the endo-contact zone.	The pegmatitic fields are associated with large tectonic zones; they are also concentrated in the places of gently-dipping contacts and convex portions of domes.
Medium erosional exposure.	The pegmatitic fields are disposed most frequently in the exo-contact zone of granitic masses, and along their extension.	The pegmatites are most frequently associated with tongues of the country-rocks which separate the individual granitic masses (lengthwise deflections of the roof).
Deep erosional exposure.	The pegmatitic fields extend along the contacts of the granitic mass, and are also associated with deep depressions of the intrusion roof, with portions of synclinal folds of the enclosing rocks, compressed between granites. Commonly they are localized in the sites where xenoliths and hybrid rocks are developed.	The pegmatites are most abundant in the places of gently-dipping contacts of the granitic masses and in the large residual bodies of the roof in granites.

Tasks in the Large-scale (1/10,000–1/25,000) Prospecting Within the Limits of the Beryl-bearing Pegmatitic Field

The main task in the geological survey work for beryllium in the scale 1/10,000–1/25,000, conducted within the limits of the beryl-bearing pegmatitic fields, is the detection and mapping of the places of accumulation of promising pegmatites, for the purpose of organizing preliminary exploration in these sites.

The prospection in the scale referred to above is based mainly on the structural-tectonic and petrographical features. The main factor determining the condition of localization of the individual groups of pegmatites within the limits of the pegmatitic field is the controlling part played by the structural elements of the enclosing rocks. A characteristic feature is the elongated shape of pegmatitic deposits in accordance with the main structural elements of the enclosing rocks, owing to which the width of the individual pegmatite-bearing zones usually varies from 0.2 to 0.5 km (less frequently to 1.5 km), while the

length varies from 1 km to several tens of kilometers. Besides a frequent connection between the pegmatitic deposits and the tectonic shear zones, this
nature of the pegmatite-bearing zones is explained by the observed regular
association of these zones with definite structures. The favorable structures
are, in particular, the cores of anticlinal folds, which carry at depth the apical
apophyses of the granite intrusion and, less frequently, the cores and limbs of
compressed synclinal folds.

The prospection carried out in the extension of the structure which controls
the pegmatitic zone (the width of the belt in question usually does not exceed
0.5 to 2 km) often results in the discovery of new deposits. Particularly interesting in this case are the sites of the fold crests and of the trend-change in the
tectonic zones and the structural elements of the enclosing rocks, which create
favorable conditions for the formation of cavities occupied by the pegmatite
melt.

The task in the large-scale prospecting also includes the details of the positive
prospecting features disclosed in the process of the geological survey and prospection work in the scale 1/100,000–1/200,000.

Besides the exo- and endo-contact zones, the subjects of particularly detailed
study are the deflections of the roof of the intrusion body, which are expressed
by the presence among granites of residual bodies of the country rocks or of a
large number of small xenoliths. Such zones within the limits of a granite
intrusion commonly are the sites of a considerable concentration of pegmatitic
formations. A thorough study should also be made of the gently-dipping contacts of the intrusive body—easily recognizable by the tortuous outline of the
contact line which forms deep 'gulfs' and tongues. Sites that present favorable
conditions for the concentration of pegmatites are the tongues of the roof,
which deeply enter the granite mass.

A positive prospection feature is the presence, in the juxta-contact zone of
the pegmatitic intrusion, of basic or ultra-basic rocks (gabbro, amphibolites),
in which, owing to their competent nature during the formation of folds,
cracked and weakened zones are produced, that are suitable for the formation
of large-size pegmatites. (see Figs. 10, 11.) This feature is characteristic of many
pegmatitic fields, where the largest beryl-bearing pegmatites are related to the
masses of the basic or ultrabasic rocks. The presence of ultrabasic rocks in the
exo-contact of a granite mass should also stimulate the attention of the geologist
as regards the possibility of finding in these sites beryl-bearing pegmatites of
the crossing-line. In such a case a very favorable feature is the presence of
vein plagioclase and fine-micaceous formations.

Nor should one overlook some geomorphological features while prospecting
for beryl-bearing pegmatites. In particular, a characteristic feature of a series
of areas is the relative resistance of pegmatitic bodies to weathering compared

with the enclosing metamorphic rocks. In such a case, the pegmatite dikes and stocks stand out sharply in relief in the form of thick ridges, walls, and domes, which can be observed not only during the usual prospection survey work, but also by means of an aerophotogrammetric survey, given suitable conditions (absence of forests, etc.).

Prospecting for Non-pegmatitic Beryllium Deposits

The prospecting features pointing to the presence of deposits of beryllium minerals, connected with tungsten- or tin-bearing greisens and quartz veins, do not differ in practice from the criteria used in prospecting for the corresponding deposits of tungsten and tin.

Methods of prospecting for the deposits of this type are explained in a number of papers (Kosov and Ostromenetskii, 1949; Nikol'skii, 1954; Smirnov, 1954); therefore, they are dealt with only briefly in the present publication.

Unlike pegmatites, most of the greisen and vein hydrothermal-pneumatolytic beryllium deposits are connected with the areas of development of small intrusions of an acidic and hyperacidic composition, that commonly are markedly changed by the processes of greisenization with the participation of fluorine. A favorable prospection feature in this case is the wide development of muscovite in the granites, which even reaches the stage of enrichment of the two-mica and muscovite greisenized granites with new additions of topaz, fluorite, and tourmaline. The task of the prospection survey includes the mapping of both the granite masses and the greisenized portions within the limits of the masses. Along with the portions in which greisenized granites had developed, one should carry out a thorough study of the zones of the exo- and endocontacts between the intrusive bodies and the enclosing rocks.

The main prospection task in this case consists in the detection, within the boundaries of the area studied, of the beryllium-bearing greisen and vein bodies. The positive feature which allows one to expect beryllium minerals to be present in the greisens and veins is the presence of some minerals which usually accompany the beryl concentrations in the deposits of this group (topaz, fluorite, muscovite, wolframite, cassiterite, molybdenite, and the tungsten and molybdenum ochres).

When mapping the detected ore field one should take into account the peculiarities of its fracture-pattern, which enables the direction of further pros pecting to be rationally determined.

The skarn beryllium deposits lie in the exo-contact zone of the beryllium-bearing granitic intrusions, near the contact between the latter and the limestones and other calcareous rocks. It has been mentioned before that the characteristic feature is the relationship between the deposits of this type and the areas of development of the hydrothermal-pneumatolytic tungsten and tin deposits whereas less characteristic is the relationship between these deposits and the exo-contact zones of intrusions that contain pegmatites with beryl. Thus, the presence of limestones in the exo-contact zone of granitic masses, presumed to be beryllium-bearing, obliges the geologists to pay careful attention to the possibility of occurrence of skarn formations enriched in beryllium.

A favorable feature that points to the possible presence of beryllium minerals in the skarns is the development of the fluoritic varieties of skarn, especially of the very characteristic thinly-lamellar fluorite-magnetite variety which is often characterized by a high beryllium content. Although a wide development of beryllium-containing vesuvinite in the skarns is a general positive feature pointing to the beryllium-bearing nature of the intrusion, yet the predominance of vesuvianite has usually a negative effect on the wide occurrence of beryllium minerals; in a number of cases these minerals do not occur at all, in spite of the relatively high mean beryllium content of the skarn.

CHAPTER | 6

Preliminary Evaluation of Beryllium Deposits on the Basis of Yields Obtained During Prospecting Work

The preliminary evaluation of beryllium deposits, based on the sampling used during light exploration work and assaying of a given beryllium deposit or ore body, is carried out during the large-scale geological survey or prospection by the analysis of the structural, morphological, and texture-paragenetic peculiarities of the deposits.

Artificial exposures and, if necessary, a preliminary assay of the ore bodies to be valued are made during a detailed survey as supplementary work for the preliminary evaluation of beryllium deposits.

The artificial exposures are made allowing for the peculiarities of the deposit studied and for the possibility of obtaining a sufficient quantity of material for the preliminary assessment of the content of the useful components in the ore. The disposition of artificial exposures is usually determined by the specific requirements of geological survey and evaluation and, as a rule, it is not related

109

to any geometrical network. In a number of cases blasting is undertaken when making artificial exposures. This refers in particular to pegmatitic deposits, where it is usually impossible to collect, without explosives, a sufficiently large sample of the material.

The preliminary assay gives only a very rough idea of the content of the useful constituent in the ore, but even this information, when used together with other objective geological data, are of a great value to the geologist. The possible methods of preliminary assay during prospection will be described in another section.

Geologic Description of Pegmatitic Formations During Prospecting Operations

The preliminary evaluation of a pegmatitic deposit should be preceded by a detailed geological description of each pegmatite. For the most interesting pegmatites it is also obligatory to make a preliminary map.

The Plan of the Field Description of Rare-metal Pegmatites During the Prospection and Examination

Geological-morphological Description

1. Composition and nature of the country rocks, and their occurrence. Relationship between pegmatites and any structural elements of the country rocks.

2. Shape of the pegmatite (vein, vein with a bulge, vein of irregular form, plate-shaped vein, lens, dike, stock).

3. Dimensions of the pegmatite (length along the strike, thickness in the bulge and at the sides, approximate mean thickness).

4. Directional structures (azimuth of the trend, mean azimuth of dip, accurate determination of the angles of dip of the hanging-wall and footwall).

5. Nature of structures in the country rocks (interbedded body or transgressing body; if the latter, then at what angle the body intersects the strike and dip of the country rocks).

6. Presence of post-pegmatitic dislocations in the pegmatite and their structures.

Mineralogical Description

1. Nature of the change of the enclosing rocks at the contact with pegmatite. Thickness of the aureole. Presence of xenoliths of the country rocks in the vein, and the nature of their alteration.

2. Texture of the pegmatite and the degree of differentiation (undiffer-

entiated, small-block, large-block, fully differentiated, replacement texture).

3. Zoning of the pegmatites:

(a) Zones of primary crystallization: pegmatoid granite (in streaky pegmatites); aplitic fringe at the contact (not to be confused with the zone of saccharoidal albite); graphic; medium- and coarse-grained quartz-feldspar of apographic or pegmatoid structure; small-block pegmatite; block microcline; block quartz; quartz spodumene).

(b) Replacement zones: muscovitic (quartz-muscovite or albite-muscovite replacement complexes); albitic (cleavelandite, fine-lamellar or saccharoidal albite); lepidolite (quartz-lepidolite or albite-lepidolite replacement complexes); greisen (fine-mica replacement complex).

4. Detailed description of the zones:

(a) Mineralogical composition and structure of the zone—rock-forming minerals, rare or accessory minerals (beryl and other rare-metal minerals are described in more detail), mean sizes of mineral segregations, their shape and visible inter-relationships with surrounding minerals.

(b) Nature of the development of the zone in the pegmatite—is it maintained along the whole vein, or does it occur in separate portions only and with what parts of the pegmatite is it associated? If it is maintained along the whole vein, the mean thickness of the zone should be indicated; if it is developed intermittently, the dimensions of these portions should be given; the approximate proportion (in percent) of the area of vein exposure, occupied by the zone; the nature of the boundaries between the zone and other zones (sharp or diffuse, straight, or tortuous).

(c) The nature of distribution of rare-metal minerals in the zone (uniform, non-uniform, in pockets, individual grains); with what part of the zone are they associated? Is there a close association between the rare-metal minerals and any vein minerals? If possible, a determination, even if only approximate, is carried out of the content of the useful minerals in the zone.

4'. Supplementary remarks relating to zones:

(a) Note the nature of transition from the aplitic zone to the enclosing rocks (sharp, gradual).

(b) Pay special attention to the presence or absence of signs of albitization within the zone of graphic pegmatite.

(c) Pay attention to the degree of albitization in the zone of the medium- and coarse-grained quartz-feldspar pegmatite, and to the presence of rare-metal minerals, even if in negligible proportions only.

(d) In the zones of small-block pegmatite and block microcline special attention should be paid to the portions of block microcline adjacent to block quartz, because in these portions one usually observes the concentration of the rare-metal minerals. Note the extent of change caused in block microcline by muscovitization and albitization.

(e) Pay attention to the form of the block-quartz zone (continuous, beaded, separated blocks, transgressing bodies) and, in particular, to the boundaries between this and the surrounding zones. If rare-metal minerals occur in the block-quartz zone, it should be noted with which side of the zone (pendant or recumbent) they are associated. Give the characteristics of the replacement of potassium feldspar at the boundary with block quartz.

(f) Establish whether the muscovite zone is isolated in the form of a fringe round the block-quartz zone, if it lies nearer to the selvages of the vein, and in what side of the vein there is greater development of the muscovite zone. Have the rare-metal minerals present in this zone undergone any change? Can a relationship between the zone and fracturing be observed?

(g) Albite zone. What variety of albite (cleavelandite, fine-lamellar, or saccharoidal) predominates in the various portions of the vein? Are there macroscopically-visible microcline relics? Have the ore-minerals of the albite zone, in particular beryl, undergone a change, and to what extent?

(h) After what zone has the lepidolite zone developed? Quartz-spodumene, albite, etc.? What is the relationship between quartz, lepidolite, and albite in the zone? Have the ore-minerals of the zone been changed, and to what extent?

(i) Pay special attention to the presence of tantalo-niobates in the greisen zone.

5. The extent of hypergenic change of the exposed part of pegmatite, and the possibility of accumulation of placers near the pegmatites.

6. Brief conclusion with respect to the commercial value of the vein.

The investigation of the individual pegmatites is accompanied by the study of the structure of the pegmatitic field and of the distribution of pegmatites within the field. It is of paramount importance to elucidate the following questions:

1. What magmatic rocks are developed within the field or near it; the nature of distribution of pegmatites with respect to the outcrops of magmatic rocks?

2. What is the relationship between the pegmatitic field and the fracture-pattern or any structure of the rocks of the intrusion roof?

3. What is the relationship between the pegmatitic field and any lithological horizon?

4. Are the pegmatites within the pegmatitic field controlled by any fracture patterns?

Morphological Factors in the Evaluation of Beryl-bearing Pegmatites

The morphological peculiarities and dimensions of pegmatites are, along with their textural-paragenetic peculiarities, the most important factors which determine the commercial prospects of a pegmatitic deposit.

During the geological survey work one frequently comes across beryl-bearing bodies with a well pronounced zonal structure and widely-developed replacement phenomena, but the small dimensions of these bodies or the unfavorable morphological features render them of little or no commercial value.

At the same time one encounters fairly frequently cases when pegmatites of considerable dimensions, endowed with highly favorable morphological features, are found to be composed of unpromising modifications which result in their being valueless.

Thus, when carrying out the preliminary evaluation of the deposits during the prospection work, one has to take into account both groups of factors referred to above, since one of them without the other cannot be used as a basis for an unequivocal judgement of the prospects of the deposit.

Proceeding from the geological prospection for beryl-bearing pegmatites, one can separate the following morphological groups of pegmatites.

1. Vein and lenticular bodies extending for less than 100 m and less than 5 m thick. These are usually of no practical interest, except the extremely rare cases when their beryl content is abnormally high.

2. Vein and lenticular bodies extending for 100 to 200 m, the mean thickness being 5 to 10 m. Single bodies with commercial beryl content usually have no independent practical value (except the very rare bodies with an abnormally high mean content). The bodies of this category are usually valued for small-scale working. A considerable number of such bodies concentrated near each other may be of commercial interest.

3. Vein, lenticular and dike-shaped bodies extending for more than 200 m, the mean thickness exceeding 10 m. In the case of a commercially interesting beryl content these can become independent economic propositions.

4. Stock-shaped pegmatites with an area of up to 2,000 m². As in (2).

5. Stock-shaped pegmatites with an area exceeding 2,000 m². As in (3).

In a number of cases the study of the morphological peculiarities of the pegmatitic formations may be of help in the evaluation of the pegmatite in depth.

The following structural features of the contacts between pegmatites and the enclosing rocks can serve for this purpose.

1. Contacts of the pegmatite dip outwardly in various directions, or the dip of the contact of the footwall is steeper than that of the contact of the hanging-wall (Fig. 36, II–II). With increasing depth the thickness of the pegmatite increases, and a bulge is possible.

2. Contacts of the pegmatite dip inwards in various directions or the dip of the contact of the footwall is gentler than in the case of the hanging-wall (Fig. 36, III–III). With increasing depth the thickness of the pegmatite decreases, and a pinch or tapering-out is possible.

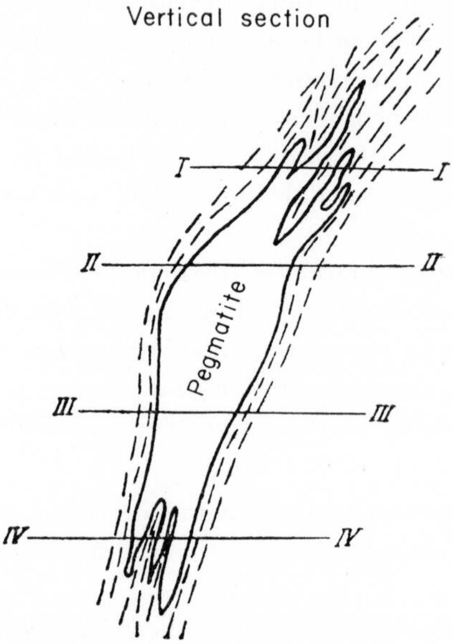

3. Contacts of the pegmatite dip parallel to each other. No unequivocal conclusion can be arrived at.

As shown in Vlasov's investigations (1943), the shape of the beryl-bearing pegmatites is of particular importance in the evaluation.

The analysis of the available facts shows that pegmatitic formations of the isometric or nearly isometric shape (stocks, pipes) and thick lenticular bodies (Figs. 10, 11, 12c, 12d) are the most promising as regards the presence of higher beryl concentrations. The presence of dome-shaped crests in the bulges of pegmatites (Fig. 6) should be noted as a particularly favorable morphological feature. Such crests commonly are characterized by an exceptionally high concentration of beryllium and contain the main mass of beryl in the given pegmatite. For example, in the dome-shaped bulge (Fig. 6) of a pegmatitic vein, which lies in a gently-dipping contraction fracture of the endo-contact part of the granite intrusion, there was found about 5 percent of beryl, and the weight of single beryl crystals attained 1.5 tons. Beyond the dome-shaped bulge the beryl content of the vein did not exceed 0.1–0.2 percent.

Increased beryl concentrations are also noted in the ordinary bulges of pegmatitic veins (Fig. 12b). Outside the bulge the beryl content in the slightly-replaced block pegmatites usually undergoes a sharp drop. At the same time in a number of cases the fully albitized necks of the vein bodies in replaced pegmatites also are found to be beryl-bearing.

Fig. 36. Contact features of the pegmatite, depending on the depth of its erosional exposure (diagram).

Textural-paragenetic Factors in the Evaluation of Beryl-bearing Pegmatites Based on Outcrops

The close relationship between beryl and the definite paragenetic complexes of pegmatitic formations enables the geologist to carry out, during inspection and mapping of the surface exposures of granitic pegmatites, the preliminary evaluation of their beryl-bearing properties, by choosing the most promising pegmatites for the intended prospection (Table 22).

In this case the preliminary evaluation of the beryl-bearing properties of a pegmatite should be based on the analysis of its paragenetic features which are reflected in the mineralogical composition and its zoning.

PLAN OF EVALUATION OF THE BERYL-BEARING PROPERTIES OF VARIOUS TYPES OF GRANITIC PEGMATITES

Graphic and kindred medium- and coarse-grained pegmatites.

↓

Have no independent commercial importance even when beryl is present.

Block and fully-differentiated layered pegmatites.

↓

Main feldspar.

↓ ↓

Medium plagioclase.   Microcline.

↓ ↘

Small-block texture.   Large-block and layered texture.

↓ ↓ ↓

Have no independent industrial importance, even when beryl is present.   Positive feature.

Replaced pegmatites.

↓

Main feldspar —albite.

↓

Positive feature.

Since the unalbitized or the weakly-albitized zones of the graphic medium- and coarse-grained pegmatite usually do not contain commercial concentrations of beryl, a predominant development of these zones in a pegmatite serves as a basis for its elimination as being beryl-bearing. An exception in this case can be a strongly albitized and muscovitized medium-grained pegmatite whose evaluation should be done with great care, because its structure might change at depth. From this point of view it is necessary to study all available mineralogical and geological data. (See the following section: "Principles of evaluation of the beryl-bearing pegmatites in depth during prospection work.")

It must be noted that small, strongly-albitized, medium-grained pegmatites that contain increased concentrations of beryl, might be of some interest for being mined in the exploration-exploitation undertakings.

The small-block pegmatites, moreover, usually do not show much promise, although in some cases they might include individual large crystals and druses of beryl, which lie within a pegmatite of small-block texture. When such pegmatites are present in considerable quantities and not far from each other, it may become possible to open-cast the individual sites rich in beryl. However, in view of the low beryl content and its highly irregular distribution, the mining of such pegmatites in depth is, as a rule, unprofitable.

When the pegmatites have large dimensions and contain increased beryl concentrations, the pegmatites with *large-block texture* may become commercial objects of some interest. In such pegmatites the portions where beryl concentration is increased are the boundary portions of the block-quartz zone and of the surrounding zone of block microcline or of medium-grained pegmatite. In individual cases beryl concentrates also at the boundary between the block-microcline zone and the next outward zone composed of medium-grained pegmatite. Thus, a wide development of the block-quartz and block-microcline zones in the pegmatite enables (always taking the dimensions of the pegmatite into account) a preliminary positive evaluation of a given pegmatite to be carried out, by isolating it for surface prospection and assaying in order to determine the beryl content in the ore zone.

The above considerations apply even more to the *fully differentiated (layered) pegmatites* which, within a series of pegmatitic fields are the most promising and contain a considerable proportion of the beryl resources so far known.

The *replaced pegmatites* in the beryl-bearing pegmatitic fields are, as a rule, the most complex and, at the same time, commercially promising formations deserving special attention.

The replaced muscovite-albite pegmatites characterized by a wide development of muscovitization and albitization of the block microcline and medium-grained pegmatite can contain increased concentrations of beryl in various portions of the pegmatite:

1. in the peripheral portions of the block-quartz zone (generation characteristic of block-texture pegmatites);

2. in albitized block microcline near segregations of block quartz;

3. in albitized medium-grained pegmatite at its boundary with the block-quartz or block-microcline zone;

4. in the endo-contact portions of the pegmatite, in the case when albitization extends along the contacts of the pegmatitic body;

5. near the contact with xenoliths of the enclosing rocks;

Table 22   *Prospecting indications of beryl in granitic pegmatites*

TYPES OF PEGMATITES	SMALL-BLOCK MICROCLINE	LARGE-BLOCK AND FULLY-DIFFERENTIATED MICROCLINE	REPLACED
Usual disposition of the ore zone.	Individual crystals and druses among small-block pegmatite, commonly in quartz blocks. Sometimes in the albitized medium-grained pegmatite.	At the boundary between the block-quartz zone and the zone of block microcline or medium-grained pegmatite; less commonly in block quartz or in albitized medium-grained pegmatite at the boundary with the block zone.	*Zone a* At the boundary between segregations of block quartz and the albite zone. *Zone b* In albitized block microcline near block-quartz segregations. *Zone c* In muscovite zone (quartz-muscovite or albite-muscovite complex). *Zone d* In medium-grained albitized pegmatite at the boundary with the block-microcline or quartz zone. *Zone e* In albite (cleavelandite) zone at the boundary of quartz-spodumene zone. *Zone f* In lepidolite zone. *Zone g* In albitized pegmatite in the endo-contact of veins or at the contact with xenoliths.
Main minerals of the ore zone.	Quartz, microcline, muscovite, albite.	Quartz, microcline, muscovite, albite.	*Zones a, b, g* Quartz, albite, muscovite. *Zone c* Quartz, muscovite, albite.

Table 22 | *Prospecting indications of beryl in granitic pegmatites (cont.)*

TYPES OF PEGMATITES	SMALL-BLOCK MICROCLINE	LARGE-BLOCK AND FULLY-DIFFERENTIATED MICROCLINE	REPLACED
Characteristic accessory minerals of beryl-bearing zones.	Apatite.	Triphylite (after it, in the oxidation zone—heterosite, graftonite and other iron and manganese phosphates; apatite).	*Zone d* Quartz, albite, muscovite, microcline relics. *Zone e* Cleavelandite, quartz. *Zone f* Lepidolite, quartz, albite. *Zones a, b, g* Triphylite (after it, in oxidation zone—heterosite and other iron and manganese phosphates). *Zone c* Bismuth minerals. *Zone e* Spessartite, lithiophilite (after it purpurite), green tourmaline. *Zone f* Rose and colorless tourmaline. *Zone g* Black tourmaline.
Nature of beryl.	In the block zones well-developed crystals: green, blue, bluish-green, in a number of cases translucent or transparent. In medium-grained pegmatite poorly developed, commonly "stuffed" crystals.		*Zones a, g* Poorly-formed crystals, sometimes of irregular or sharply pyramidal form. Color from pale-green to white, sometimes cream. *Zone b* Poorly-formed crystals, commonly in the form of a sharp truncated pyramid. Color pale-green, yellow-green, pale-yellow.

TYPES OF PEGMATITES	SMALL-BLOCK MICROCLINE	LARGE-BLOCK AND FULLY-DIFFERENTIATED MICROCLINE	REPLACED
			Zone c Small crystals, usually of irregular shape, frequently translucent. Color green, pale-green, bluish. *Zone d* Poorly-formed crystals of sharply pyramidal form. Usually "stuffed" with albite, quartz, muscovite. *Zone e* Short-prismatic (to tabular) crystals; white, yellowish, or rose. *Zone f* Irregular or short-prismatic, colorless or rose crystals. Commonly translucent to perfectly transparent.
Associated useful minerals of the beryl-bearing zones.	Columbite, tantalite.	Columbite, tantalite.	*Zones a, b, c, g* Columbite-tantalite. *Zone e* Mangano-tantalite, mangano-columbite, microlite, spodumene, cassiterite, pollucite. *Zone f* Mangano-columbite, mangano-tantalite, microlite, stibio-tantalite, bismutho-tantalite, cassiterite, pollucite, lepidolite.

6. in the segregations of the muscovite zone, composed of the quartz-muscovite or albite-muscovite replacement complex.

The replaced spodumene-albite and lepidolite-albite pegmatites can contain commercially valuable concentrations of beryl in the same portions as the muscovite-albite pegmatites.

Instead of the early generation of green or bluish-green beryl, characteristic of the block pegmatites, increased concentrations of alkali-beryl of the rosterite-vorobyevite group are known to occur in the replaced pegmatites of the spodumene-albite type at the boundary with the quartz-spodumene core. In a number of places the same beryl varieties form concentrations in the lepidolite zone.

The complex nature of the beryl deposits related to the replaced spodumene-albite pegmatites makes it possible to isolate deposits of this type as first and foremost objects for prospecting.

Replaced lepidolite-albite pegmatites are relatively rare in the beryl-bearing pegmatitic fields. As the extreme members of the evolutionary series of the granitic pegmatites, they contain all beryl-bearing complexes characteristic of replaced pegmatites. Large pegmatites with a wide development of the lepidolite zone undoubtedly deserve a positive evaluation and the organization of prospection work.

Principles of Evaluation of Beryl-bearing Pegmatites in Depth During Prospection

The preliminary evaluation of the beryl-bearing pegmatites in depth during prospecting is connected with considerable difficulties, because the geologist who carries out the evaluation must take into account the whole complex group of factors that determine the vertical zoning of the pegmatites. Nevertheless, in a number of cases, even when all required conditions have been satisfied, it is impossible to obtain an unequivocal valuation result without carrying out mining or drilling operations.

The main textural-paragenetic and morphological features that enable the nature of zonal variation of this or that type of pegmatite at depth to be approximately estimated are:

1. Erosion has exposed a graphic or medium-grained pegmatite without any replacement features. The analysed horizon most probably represents the 'root' part of the pegmatitic injection. There are no grounds to expect that the differentiation will improve with increasing depth.

2. In the examined outcrop of the medium-grained pegmatite, noticeable features of albitization and muscovitization, and the presence of beryl have

been observed. Particularly strong albitization is observed at the contacts. This case presents great difficulties as regards interpretation. To obtain a well-defined idea of the possibility of a change, with depth, of the zonation of the pegmatite, considerable help can be found if one considers its morphological peculiarities. Three cases are possible.

(a) The contacts of the pegmatite dip outwards in different directions, or the dip of the footwall is steeper than that of the hanging-wall. In this case one can expect that, with increasing depth, the thickness of the pegmatite will increase and its degree of differentiation will be intensified. The expediency of starting light prospecting or drilling operations for making the evaluation more accurate depends in this case on a number of factors:

(1) presence and concentration of beryl at the outcrop of the pegmatite;

(2) dimensions of the pegmatite;

(3) degree of alteration in the medium-grained pegmatite, caused by the albitization process; this allows an estimation to be made of the intensity of development of the replacement processes at depth;

(4) economic conditions of the site.

(b) The contacts of the pegmatite dip parallel to each other. In this case it is difficult to arrive at an unequivocal conclusion, because a partial albitization of medium-grained pegmatite in individual deposits has been observed in the 'roots' of strongly albitized pegmatitic bodies composed at the upper horizons of the replaced muscovite-albite or spodumene-albite pegmatite; it is also possible that this albitization was caused by the penetration of barren albitizing solutions from the granitic magma. The expediency of starting light prospecting or drilling operations depends on the same factors as those mentioned in point 1.

(c) The contacts of the pegmatite dip inwards in various directions or else the dip of the footwall is gentler than that of the hanging-wall. In this case one can expect a decrease of thickness with increasing depth. It is difficult to reach an unequivocal conclusion without having supplementary data which can be obtained by studying more accurately the morphology of the pegmatite, using prospection pits or drill-cores. The decrease of thickness may indicate as well, a rapid thinning-out of the pegmatite as a contraction followed by another bulge. Practice shows that, in the case of a contraction, albitization is shown extremely strongly, attaining the complete replacement of medium-grained pegmatite with finely-crystalline albite.

3. Surface exposure of small-block pegmatite without noticeable signs of albitization. Examples of investigation of such pegmatites show that, at depth,

there is usually a thickening of the outer zones composed of graphic or medium-grained pegmatite, associated with the decrease of the small-block zone. At the same time the small-block type of pegmatite is gradually replaced at depth by the medium-grained or graphic type.

4. In the outcrop of a beryl-bearing small-block pegmatite one observes a noticeable development of albitization and muscovitization. Just as in the previously analyzed case of albitized medium-grained pegmatites, the given outcrop may be the apical part of a well-differentiated pegmatite which, in a number of cases, is found to be more interesting at depth as regards the beryl content. On the other hand, the outcrop may be the 'root' portion of an intensely replaced pegmatite whose most interesting upper horizons have already been destroyed by erosion.

The recognition of this situation is usually made as a result of detailed study of the contact morphology; from the nature of these contacts it is possible to determine in a number of cases whether the thickness of the pegmatite increases or decreases with increasing depth. An important part in the correct evaluation is also played by the determination of the degree of albitization of the exposed horizon. Practice shows that the albitization of the small-block apical portions of the block and layered pegmatites is usually shown with greater intensity than in the 'roots' of replaced pegmatites.

In the former case the replacement complex has a coarser texture; quite characteristic also is the presence of minerals of the phosphate group, the presence of druses of scaly muscovite, and in some pegmatites an increased tourmaline content was observed.

It should be noted that the expediency of exploration of both the medium-grained and the small-block pegmatites, which, from the data of surface inspection, are supposed to have an improved degree of differentiation and intensification of mineralization at depth, should be very carefully substantiated, in each specific case, by an analysis and a comparison of all positive and negative factors which affect the evaluation. In doubtful cases it is very desirable to carry out relatively shallow drilling (one or two boreholes for every pegmatitic body) or to provide individual prospecting pits, which usually enables the morphology of the pegmatite to be determined with greater accuracy, and the nature of zonal change at depth to be demonstrated.

5. A block or layered (fully-differentiated) muscovite-microcline pegmatite is exposed at the surface. If beryl is present in suitable concentrations, such pegmatites represent, in a number of cases, valuable commercial beryl deposits. The valuer's task in this case consists in determining the depth of occurrence of the beryl-bearing ore zone related to the well-differentiated pegmatite. The analysis of the available facts shows that the principal factors governing the zonal constancy of the block and layered pegmatites with depth are the dimen-

sions and morphological features of the pegmatite. The beryl mineralization related to large-block zones has been traced down to a depth of about 80 m along the dip, by investigating the individual large dike-shaped bodies (thickness in excess of 20 m, length in excess of 250 m) composed of large-block well-differentiated pegmatite. At the same time there exist many examples showing that small pegmatites up to 20 m thick and extending for up to 100 m change their zoning at a depth of 10–30 m less abruptly and pass into the small-block pegmatite with a low beryl content. It should be noted that, compared with the steeply-dipping pegmatites, the gently-dipping ones are characterized, as a rule, by a more constant zoning. All these examples point to the necessity of a selective study of the ore bodies by means of boreholes, vertical exploration shafts, or galleries—given a favorable relief.

A favorable feature that indicates the exposed horizon of the block or layered pegmatite to be near the apical portion of the pegmatite body is the wide development of the albite and muscovite replacement complexes, and the presence of triphylite and other iron and manganese phosphates.

6. At the exposed horizon, the pegmatite is represented by replaced muscovite-albite pegmatite in which the block-microcline zone has been fully or almost fully albitized. From the point of view of the beryl content, this type, as already mentioned, is a very promising one. When such pegmatites are explored in deep natural sections, one observes in many cases a transition to the muscovite-microcline pegmatites, which takes place by a gradual reduction in albitization. The depth of spread of the ore zone in the replaced muscovite-albite pegmatites depends, as in the preceding case, mainly on the dimensions and morphological features of the pegmatite; however, other conditions being equal, it is greater than in the block muscovite-microcline pegmatites.

7. The nature of the zonal variation of the replaced spodumene-albite pegmatites with depth depends also on their dimensions and morphology.

Cases are known where lenticular pegmatites of spodumene-albite composition extending for about 100 m and having a thickness of about 20 m in the bulge, abruptly changed their zonation at depth of 10 to 15 m. The zonal change consisted of a noticeable decrease in the amount of spodumene in the quartz-spodumene zone and in the appearance of large blocks of microcline-perthite in the quartz core. The pegmatite type became more similar to the muscovite-albite variety. The beryl-bearing albite zone that contains quartz-muscovite pockets was found here to have a constant thickness, but the beryl content became lower (Fig. 22).

An exceptional constancy of zonation with increasing depth is, in turn, characteristic of a large stock-shaped spodumene-albite pegmatite, up to 100 × 300 m in dimension. One of several large deposits of this type, endowed with a very distinct concentric zonation, did not reveal, when investigated by means of bore-holes to a depth of over 250 m, any zonal change. The beryl-bearing ore zone which lies at the boundary between the block-microcline zone and the strongly albitized outer zone of the medium-grained pegmatite was also found to remain constant as regards beryl content (Fig. 22).

Thus the large beryl-bearing pegmatites represented by the replaced spodumene-albite varieties are usually promising at depth where, according to the available data, many pass into the replaced muscovite-albite pegmatites.

8. The replaced lepidolite-albite and greisen-albite pegmatites are usually the upper, apical horizons of the pegmatitic injection, which, as depth increases, change into spodumene-albite or muscovite-albite pegmatites.

In this connection such pegmatite types are, as a rule, promising at depth, and ought to be explored by deep drilling.

Just as in the preceding cases, the principal factors which determine the prospects of each specific pegmatitic body are its dimensions and morphological peculiarities.

Well-differentiated and intensely replaced large pegmatites have in many cases in their apical part a well-developed lepidolite-albite or greisen-albite "cap." At the same time, in small pegmatites the lepidolite or greisen zone ends in some cases at a depth of 3 to 10 m where it passes into a barren pegmatite of little interest, while in other cases it can be traced without any noticeable change to a depth of 100 to 150 m. The latter case refers in particular to pegmatitic veins which were formed in mobile tectonic zones when replacement solutions entered more than once from deep horizons.

Thus, to determine conjecturally the prospects of each individual pegmatitic deposit in depth, it is necessary for the geologist, during the prospection phase of geological work, to analyze thoroughly the entire complex of the textural-mineralogical, geochemical, and morphological factors which determine the conditions of formation.

It has been mentioned already that conclusions based on one or two factors without taking into account other peculiarities of the deposit usually lead to errors which in many cases result in a wrong direction being given to the geological prospecting operations.

The checking of assumptions regarding the prospects of pegmatitic deposits in depth should, at first, be carried out, only selectively, by means of bore-holes or mine workings (prospecting pits, galleries).

Fundamental Principles of Evaluation of Non-pegmatitic Deposits Based on Outcrops During Prospecting Work

As in the evaluation of the deposits of any other type, the preliminary evaluation of the greisen, quartz vein, and skarn beryllium-bearing formations aims in the first place at a determination of the size of the deposit, which is governed by the number and dimensions of the ore-bearing bodies and by their mean content of beryllium minerals.

Since the preliminary evaluation of the beryl content in wolframite-quartz and cassiterite-quartz deposits usually presents a much easier task than in the case of the pegmatite-type deposits, the evaluation of such deposits from outcrops during prospection work is mainly reduced to the analysis of the morphological peculiarities and dimensions of the ore-bodies. The deposits of the group under consideration are usually characterized by small (compared with the pegmatites) dimensions of the veins and by their relatively high content of beryllium minerals. While a mean beryl content of 1 percent very rarely occurs in pegmatites, the beryl concentrations commonly encountered in the hydro-thermal-pneumatolytic beryl-bearing vein formations are measured by several percent or even several tens of percents. As has been said in the general part of this work, the highest concentrations of beryllium minerals, attaining 75 to 100 percent, are characteristic of thin veins and short streaks. Turning towards the valuation of such rich beryllium-bearing formations, one should note that, according to a simple arithmetical computation, a beryl streak 2 cm thick, containing 50 to 100 percent of exploitable beryl, is equivalent as regards beryl resources to a beryl-bearing pegmatite vein of the same length, containing 0.2 percent of beryl and having a thickness of 5 to 10 m.

In the evaluation of the greisen and vein deposits of this group, it is very important to elucidate the crystal dimensions of beryllium minerals and their interrelations with other minerals, because these factors play a main part in determining the feasible method of beneficiating the ores.

Finally, passing over to the beryllium-bearing formations of the skarn type, one should note the special difficulties of the evaluation of such deposits in the field caused by the extremely small grain-size of the beryllium minerals in the skarns and by the difficulty of their identification which is usually impossible without special microchemical and optical methods. While an approximate evaluation of the helvite and danalite content in the skarns can be made in the field after a suitable processing of the crushed samples for obtaining the stain reaction with arsenic or antimony and counting the grains of helvite-danalite under the binocular microscope, one can obtain some definite data about the presence of other beryllium minerals in skarns, especially chrysoberyl and phenacite, only after a detailed laboratory investigation of the samples taken. Consequently, the preliminary evaluation of a skarn deposit whose beryllium-bearing nature is either known or presumed consists essentially in the evaluation of distribution of the promising skarn varieties. The guiding features in such evaluation may be the above-mentioned mineralogical peculiarities of beryllium-bearing skarns, e.g. the leading part played by fluorite and magnetite-

Table 23 | *Associated ore minerals in the compound beryllium deposits*

TYPE OF DEPOSIT	POSSIBLE ACCOMPANY-ING USEFUL MINERALS	REMARKS
Block and fully differentiated muscovite-microcline granitic pegmatites.	Columbite-tantalite.	Very common accompanying component of beryl deposits, mined in a number of deposits in Brazil, India, and U.S.A.
	Commercial mica (muscovite).	In the case of commercial aggregations of mica, beryl may be profitably extracted even when its content is as low as 0.1 percent.
	Ceramic raw material (feldspar, quartz).	When the utilization of ceramic raw materials from pegmatites is feasible (short distance from deposit to railway or waterway) beryl may be extracted simultaneously irrespective of its content.
	Gems (beryl, aquamarine, heliodor, vorobyevite, topaz).	In some deposits these may become valuable accessory minerals.
Replaced muscovite-albite, granitic pegmatites.	Columbite-tantalite.	Presence of tantalite or columbite in a complex with beryl considerably increases the profitability of mining the deposit.
	Commercial mica (muscovite).	Very valuable, but extremely rare (for this type) as an accompanying useful mineral.
Replaced spodumene-albite and lepidolite-albite granitic pegmatites.	Spodumene.	Valuable accompanying mineral; if it is the main component, it becomes possible to simultaneously extract beryl regardless of its content.
	Columbite-tantalite.	Very valuable accompanying ore-mineral which, in a number of cases, is the main [economic—Ed.] constituent.
	Microlite, pollucite, amblygonite, lepidolite.	Valuable accompanying useful minerals whose extraction along with beryl may ensure the profitable exploitation of the deposit.
Crossing-line pegmatites.	Emerald, alexandrite.	Highly valuable accompanying minerals.
Greisens, feldspar-quartz, and quartz veins.	Wolframite, cassiterite, molybdenite.	Beryl is the common accompanying ore-mineral. Although its extraction is at present difficult owing to micro-crystallinity, this complex source of beryl will become very important in the future.
Fluorite pneumatolytes and hydrothermalites in limestones.	Cassiterite, fluorite.	
Skarns.	Fluorite, possibly scheelite.	

fluorite varieties, the streaky texture, etc. One should also stress the need for a careful approach to the evaluation of the skarn deposits even when the results of chemical analysis of the samples point to the presence of beryllium. In a number of cases the relatively high beryllium contents in the skarns may be due to its disseminated form, present as an impurity in vesuvianite and other skarn silicates. Hence, even the preliminary evaluation of the skarns with respect to beryllium can be done only after one obtains the results of the mineralogical investigation which point to the presence of beryllium minerals in the ore-bearing body, and of laboratory beneficiation results.

Evaluation of the Possibly Complex Nature of Beryllium Deposits

The complex nature of most types of beryllium deposits has in a number of cases a decisive significance for their economic valuation. Therefore, even in the first stage of evaluation in detailed prospecting work it is necessary to study carefully and evaluate the possibility of "complex" exploitation of a deposit. Now here one can encounter a case where a deposit which is characterized by a non-commercial content of beryllium minerals but which contains some other useful mineral, may prove to be commercially interesting and whose mining may prove profitable in such a case. In particular, it is noted in the report of the Materials Policy Commission submitted to the President of the U.S.A. (Resources for Freedom, 1952) that the "compound" exploitation of beryl deposits reduces the cost of beryl extraction to one-quarter. The possibility of simultaneous beryl extraction should be studied with particular care in the case of the deposits of ceramic raw materials, emeralds, mica, lithium and tantalo-niobates in pegmatites, and in the case of the wolframite, molybdenite, and cassiterite deposits of the quartz greisens. Data relating to the complex nature of various types of beryllium deposits, which may be utilized in the preliminary evaluation of deposits is given in Table 23.

CHAPTER | 7

Methods of Exploration for Beryl Deposits

The methods of exploration for the pegmatitic beryl deposits, just as those of other pegmatite deposits, are not developed sufficiently. Unlike the latter, the exploration of beryl deposits related to quartz veins, greisens, or skarns does not differ in principle from the exploration for analogous cassiterite or wolframite deposits.

The following contains an analysis of the fundamental principles of exploration for beryl deposits, determined by their specific geological and mineralogical features.

Opening the Outcrops of Beryl-bearing Bodies

The exploration of the promising beryl-bearing bodies found during detailed prospecting work begins with the opening of the ore-bodies from the surface. Surface exploration is carried out by means of trenches, stripping, and bore-holes for the purpose of: (1) establishing the structure of the deposit, (2) establishing the texture (zoning) of pegmatites, and (3) obtaining preliminary data on the beryl content of the ore-bodies.

The structure of the deposits is established with the aid of the large-scale

128

survey (scale 1/1,000 to 1/10,000) of the geological features. In the large-scale geological survey the portions covered with detritus are opened by means of main trenches cut at right angles to the trend of the known ore bodies. Besides more accurate data of the deposit structure, the main trenches reveal in a number of cases new and parallel ore veins which is especially important in the case of the hydrothermal-pneumatolytic vein beryl deposits with quartz and wolframite. (See Fig. 33.) The distances between the main trenches are calculated depending on the dimensions and geological features of the ore bodies so as to intersect all the promising ore bodies. Usually in different stages of exploration the spacing between the trenches varies from 50 m to 300–400 m.

The structure of the pegmatites is established by preparing detailed geological plans on the scale 1/200 to 1/500, depending on the dimensions of the ore-body. The zones of the pegmatite are mapped, particular attention being paid to the correct mapping of the boundaries of the beryl-bearing paragenetic complexes.

The exploration of pegmatitic beryl deposits shows that, without preparing a detailed geological plan that reflects the zoning of the pegmatite, it is impossible to carry out a more or less correct evaluation of the deposit and to determine the rational direction of further geological-exploration work.

Without differing in principle from the usual large-scale mapping of ore formations, the mapping of the pegmatites requires attention to characteristic geological and mineralogical features. The mapping consists not only in determining the boundaries of the pegmatite and the ore zone, but also in detecting and reflecting in the plan the internal structure of the pegmatite which may be at times quite complicated.

The survey scale is chosen depending on the dimensions and complexity of the internal structure of the pegmatite.

Small pegmatites are commonly represented on the 1/200 scale, less frequently 1/100, whereas for large pegmatitic dikes and stocks the commonest scale is 1/500, less frequently (for particularly large ones) 1/1,000.

The plan of the pegmatite should correctly reflect its zoning and should serve as a basis for its classification.

The preparation of the plan is divided into four stages:

1. Plotting of the boundaries of the pegmatite on the topographical base.
2. Preparation of a number of sections across the trend of the pegmatite.
3. Plotting of sections on the plan.
4. Checking and correction of the prepared plan at the locality, and delineating zones.

The plotting of the outlines of the pegmatite on the topographical base is carried out either by eye or with instruments, depending on the aims of the survey.

In individual cases the sections can be prepared directly from the exposure of the pegmatite revealed by erosion, but for obtaining reliable sections which correctly reflect the internal structure of the pegmatite, it is usually necessary to sink trenches or to strip the surface.

The density of the section grid required for the preparation of plans may vary from 5 to 20 m depending on the dimensions and complexity of the internal structure of the pegmatite.

The sections are described in detail and are drawn on millimeter graph paper on the scale 1/50 (less frequently 1/25). The sketch shows the outlines of the paragenetic complexes and points out the areas where the ore minerals and the characteristic typomorphic minerals are positioned. Figure 37 shows an example of a typical legend for the documentation of pegmatites.

After the sections have been prepared they are plotted on the plan of the pegmatite with the corresponding scale reduction. The zone outlines in the intervals between sections are plotted by interpolation.

It is usually necessary to make the plan thus prepared more precise at the locality, using for this purpose all artificial and natural exposures occurring between the sections within the limits of the pegmatite.

The opening-up of the individual ore-bodies from the surface is most frequently carried out by means of trenches cut at right angles to the trend of the ore-body. In gently-dipping bodies the trenches are replaced by bore pits. When the detritus is very deep, the opening of ore-bodies is carried out by means of trenches. Relatively thin beryl-bearing veins (<1 m) are opened by means of ditches along the trend.

In order to establish the texture of the pegmatite and to obtain reliable data about the beryl content in the ore zone, the trenches should penetrate into the 'root' outcrop of pegmatite for at least 0.5 m. It is obvious that, in this case, one should open up the fresh part of the pegmatite, unaffected by weathering processes. A *condition sine qua non* is also the intersection of both contacts of the pegmatite. To determine correctly the structures of the contacts, in many cases it is found expedient to deepen the trench in the intersections with the endo-contact zone of the country rocks.

To prepare geological plans of pegmatites, the distance between the trenches may vary between 10 and 20 m, depending on the dimensions of the pegmatite and the complexity of its internal structure. The same distance between trenches suffices to obtain reliable data regarding the beryl content in the ore zone.

It should be noted that the exploration of beryl deposits by means of trenches is of great importance, especially in the case of small-scale ore bodies, because such exploration from the surface serves as the basis for calculating the beryl resources in category A_1.

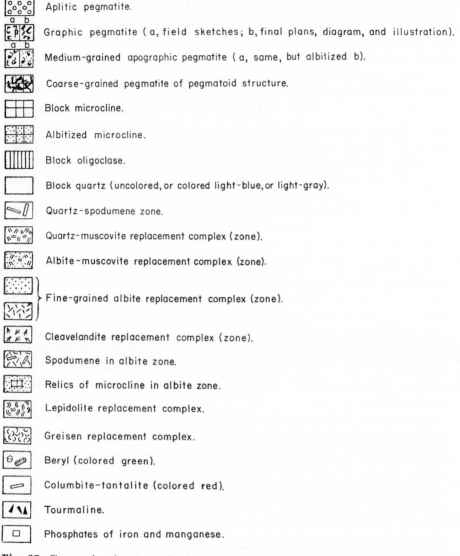

Aplitic pegmatite.

Graphic pegmatite (a, field sketches; b, final plans, diagram, and illustration).

Medium-grained apographic pegmatite (a, same, but albitized b).

Coarse-grained pegmatite of pegmatoid structure.

Block microcline.

Albitized microcline.

Block oligoclase.

Block quartz (uncolored, or colored light-blue, or light-gray).

Quartz-spodumene zone.

Quartz-muscovite replacement complex (zone).

Albite-muscovite replacement complex (zone).

Fine-grained albite replacement complex (zone).

Cleavelandite replacement complex (zone).

Spodumene in albite zone.

Relics of microcline in albite zone.

Lepidolite replacement complex.

Greisen replacement complex.

Beryl (colored green).

Columbite-tantalite (colored red).

Tourmaline.

Phosphates of iron and manganese.

Fig. 37. Conventional patterns for large-scale mapping and documentation of pegmatite formations.

As a result of the surface exploration of the deposit the following should be obtained:

1. a general geological map of the deposit (scale 1/10,000), and a detailed geological map (scale 1/1,000 or 1/2,000, depending on the geological features and dimensions of the deposit), containing data that enables obtaining unequivocal information about the structure of the deposit;

2. geological plans of ore bodies (scale 1/100–1/500, depending on the dimensions and complexity of the internal structure of the ore body); in the case of pegmatites it is necessary to plot on the plans the outlines of the para-genetic complexes (pegmatite zones); and

3. data regarding the attitude of the ore zone at outcrop and the beryl content of the ore body based on sampling data.

The results of the surface exploration serve as a basis for determining the direction of subsequent geological exploratory work and the preliminary evalua-tion of the deposit. From this data (including sampling) it is possible to carry out the assessment of the resources of the deposit in categories C_1 and C_2. Along with the result of detailed exploration at deep horizons the data of surface exploration are also used for assessing the resources of category B.

Exploration of Deposits in Depth

The exploration of beryl deposits in depth is based on the results of the surface exploration. In each specific case the choice of direction of detailed exploratory work is based on the structural features of the deposits and the internal structure of the beryl-bearing bodies established during surface exploration and recorded on geological maps and detailed plans.

The aim of exploration in this case is to trace the beryl mineralization in depth and to map the beryl-bearing ore zones at deep horizons.

The detailed exploration of beryl deposits is carried out by means of mining and bore holes.

When applied to the hydrothermal-pneumatolytic beryl deposits, the method of borehole exploration does not differ practically from the method used in the exploration of analogous quartz-wolframite greisen and vein deposits. No special remarks are necessary for the borehole method of exploration of beryl deposits related to mica-plagioclase pegmatites of the crossing-line: this method con-sists in tracing in depth the series of beryl-bearing veins (see Fig. 26). At the same time the applicability of drilling to the exploration of the common pegmatites is in some cases doubted. One usually refers here to the complexity of pegmatite structure and to the non-uniformity of distribution of the beryl mineralization in the pegmatites. However, notwithstanding these features the exploitation of the pegmatite-type beryl deposits makes it possible nowadays to recommend a wide application of drilling to the exploration of the deep horizons of pegmatitic formations.

The distinct regularities of the zonal structure of pegmatites and the constant relationship between beryl and definite complexes (zones) enable the geologist to determine unequivocally on the cores whether the beryl-bearing zone extends further in depth, whether there is a zonal change of the pegmatite, or whether a contraction of the ore-bearing paragenetic complex begins at the intersected horizon. The application of relatively shallow core-drilling in the initial stage of exploration of the pegmatitic deposit always yields very positive results, because it enables, with a minimum loss of time and money, an assessment of the deposit at deep horizons to be made and the correct direction of the underground mining work to be determined. It should be stressed that drilling will be accompanied in all cases by the detailed documentation and description of the core without which the results of drilling cannot be utilized for the evaluation of the deposit.

While recording the presence or absence of a beryl-bearing ore zone the drilling cannot, however, serve for obtaining reliable data about the beryl content in the ore zones or bodies. In this connection the data from the drilling are not applicable to assess the resources in category B.

When discussing the applicability of drilling operations to the detailed exploration of beryllium deposits, one should also stress the importance of underground drilling, the wide use of which is highly recommended. Horizontal underground drilling carried out from mine workings can be used for (1) the detection and tracing of series of parallel, relatively thin ore veins; (2) mapping the beryllium-bearing greisen bodies between mine workings; (3) defining the zonation of the pegmatite and for tracing the ore zone in the intervals between mine workings.

While providing valuable material for more precise mapping and more accurate morphology of the ore body, the boreholes of underground drilling cannot determine the beryl content. This can only be found by the assay of mine workings.

The method of exploration of beryl deposits by means of underground mine workings does not differ in principle from that of other deposits of analogous form with a non-uniform content of ore-minerals.

The exploration of steeply-dipping pegmatites is usually carried out by making a drive with crosscuts and raises (Fig. 38). In this case it is necessary that the whole thickness of the ore body be intersected by crosscuts. Zonal features of some pegmatitic beryl deposits make it necessary to make ring drives (Fig. 39).

Gently-dipping ore bodies are explored by making drives with raises and blind shafts [winzes]. Sometimes inclined galleries ('inclines') are used in the exploration of these bodies, but the complicated sinking of such workings allows these only when it is impossible to 'undercut' the ore body with a gallery or drive.

Since the exploration of beryl deposits is almost always accompanied by their tentative exploitation, it is most expedient to sink a shaft in the beryl-bearing ore zone, taking into account at the same time the possibility of utilizing

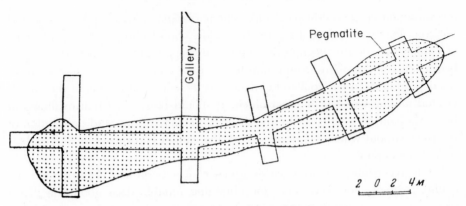

Fig. 38. Plan of the pegmatite explored by a drive with crosscuts.

the exploratory mining in the future, when the deposit will be fully exploited.

The density of the exploration network in the examination of beryl deposits by means of underground mine workings depends on the specific features of the geological structure of the given deposit. Depending on the dimensions of the ore-body, a distance is usually maintained along the vertical which equals the height from one-half to one mining level (20 to 40 m). The determination of the necessary network density along the trend depends also on the dimensions and geological features of the ore body; in any case the distance between crosscuts should not exceed 20 m.

The distance between the raises, when beryl deposits are explored in category B, is usually assumed to be 30 to 40 m depending on the dimensions and features of the ore zone. In gently-dipping bodies, where vertical raises are in practice the only type of mine workings, which intersect the entire thickness of the ore-body, the distance between the raises should not exceed 20 m.

The distance between the boreholes should be determined by the geological features of the deposit and by the problems which are expected to be solved by drilling. Depending on these factors, the distances between the boreholes usually vary from 30 to 100 m. The 50 × 50 m grid is used most frequently. At the initial stage of drilling it is indispensable to intersect at depth the portions of the ore zone, which seem to be the most interesting on the basis of the surface exploration.

Examples are given below of the application of core-drilling in the exploration of pegmatitic beryl deposits.

1. A lenticular pegmatite extending for 200 m, with a thick bulge in its central part, showed a promising beryl content as a result of the surface assays. The beryl mineralization is related to an albite zone which forms the edge of the central quartz core of the pegmatite. At the sides of the vein albitization decreases and the beryl mineralization weakens. To determine the exploitation

possibilities of the vein at depth and the direction of intensive geological-exploratory work, three inclined boreholes were drilled, each 50 to 60 m deep, with the aim of intersecting the ore body at a depth of 30 m along the dip. The central borehole was positioned at the center of the bulge, while the two end boreholes were positioned at the sides, at a distance of 60 m from the central borehole. The boreholes showed that the bulge is inclined to one side of the vein. The ore-bearing albite zone was distinctly traced along the central borehole, and also along one side of the vein in one of the end boreholes which intersected the bulge, but was absent at the other borehole where the thickness

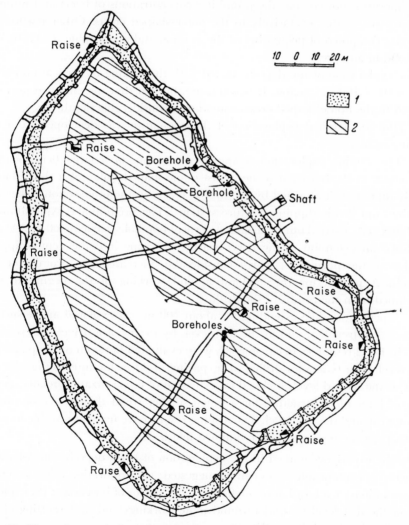

Fig. 39. Plan of a stock-shaped pegmatite explored by a ring-shaped drive with a system of crosscuts, crossdrifts, and raises. (1) Pegmatite; (2) ring-shaped drive.

of the vein diminished and the albite replacement complex was poorly developed. The bulge at the side of the vein, undercut by the borehole, was later opened by means of a gallery, where it was established that the ore zone had a commercial content of beryl.

2. A gently-dipping pegmatite vein lay conformably in crystalline schists crumpled into recumbent folds. In the cupola-shaped vein crests related to the slanting anticlinal folds of the enclosing rocks one observed an increase in the thickness of the pegmatite, a more perfect degree of differentiation, and a sign of replacement processes. The sampling results and the working of the few exposures showed that the promising concentrations of beryl and tantalo-niobates are related exclusively to the dome-shaped crests. Other portions of the vein, composed of pegmatites of the graphic and apographic structure, did not contain any ore.

The exploration of the deposit started with the sinking of vertical boreholes with a 60 $\times$ 100 m spacing. It was thus established that the enriched portions related to the dome-shaped crests extend to a considerable depth.

A plan for detailed exploration of the pegmatite was developed from the drilling results.

3. The drilling exploration of the deep horizons of a large beryl-bearing pegmatitic stock showed it to be a vast dome-shaped bulge of a thick, blind, gently-dipping vein, formed by the shift of blocks in the intersection of steeply-dipping and gently-dipping fracture systems. The preliminary exploration of the blind vein, carried out by means of vertical boreholes (spacing 60 $\times$ 100 m), disclosed an extension of the beryl-bearing ore zone into the gently-dipping portion of the pegmatite, which considerably increased the promise of the deposit. A project for the exploration and working of the pegmatite was developed from the results of the drilling.

4. A pegmatite dike extending for about 300 m was explored at the surface by means of trenches, and at the first level, by means of a drive and crosscuts from it. Beryl resources in category C_1 were evaluated between outcrop and the first level. The boreholes drilled at a spacing of 40 m for intersecting the ore body at the second level disclosed an extension of mineralization related to the zone of large-block structure for a much smaller trend than was observed at the outcrop and the first level. The drilling results have made it possible to trace the C_1-category resources to the sampled first level.

On the experience gained in the exploitation of beryl deposits the following sequence of exploration stages can be suggested: (1) exploration of the outcrop; (2) preliminary exploration of the first level by means of boreholes; (3) exploration of the first level by underground mine workings and undercutting of the succeeding level with boreholes.

CHAPTER 8

Sampling of Beryl Deposits

It is known that beryl deposits are characterized by an irregular, very irregular, or extremely irregular beryl distribution in the ore zones.

The methods of sampling beryl deposits are extremely poorly developed, owing to which the applicability of any specific method to these deposits is highly uncertain.

Some preliminary recommendations given below are based on the analytical results of exploration of various deposits, but these require further corroboration by experimental investigations.

Channel Sampling

The available data relating to attempts at applying the channel (trench) method to sampling for beryl clearly prove its unsuitability to pegmatites that contain large disseminated beryl or beryl occurring in separate nests. This is explained by the geological and mineralogical features of the majority of beryl deposits, especially by the irregular beryl distribution and by the considerable size of its crystals.

The comparative results of assaying a beryl-bearing ore zone by the channel and total analysis methods in one pegmatite (Table 24) can be adduced as an example.

Except for some hydrothermal-pneumatolytic beryl deposits characterized by

Table 24 | *Comparison of channel and total samples for beryl content*

| | BERYL CONTENT, % | |
NO. OF SAMPLE	TRENCH SAMPLE	TOTAL SAMPLE
1	0.0	0.687
2	0.0	0.848
3	0.0	0.306
4	0.0	0.0
5	0.0	0.687
6	0.0	0.0
7	0.0	0.0
8	0.0	0.246
9	0.0	0.0
10	15.5	0.569
11	0.0	0.177
12	0.0	0.0
13	0.0	0.162
14	1.25	0.215
15	0.0	0.672
16	0.0	0.0
17	1.15	0.295
18	0.0	0.516

microcrystallinity and by a more uniform distribution of the ore-mineral, the problem of the applicability of the channel method obviously cannot be solved unequivocally and requires experimental checking.

"Scratch" Sampling

The 'scratch' method of sampling showed good results in a number of beryl deposits, and its application is mainly limited by the high cost and time-consuming nature of the sample selection (it should be noted that, as regards cohesion and hardness, the rocks of beryl deposits belong to categories from VI to X). This method can be recommended for deposits of finely disseminated beryllium ores which do not require further ore picking, and for pegmatitic deposits in which the application of the grab-sampling method referred to below causes difficulties, for some reasons.

The samples are taken from separate sections, across the trend of the ore complexes, taking into account the zonal nature of the beryl-bearing body. It is indispensable to sample the entire thickness of the ore zone along the given cross-section. The 'scratches' are usually taken along the wall of the working or the bottom of the trench; the width of the 'scratch' is 0.5 m, the section length 1 to 2 m, the depth 10 cm. When using the 'scratch' method for the sampling of thin ore-bodies or zones, the width of the 'scratch' depends on their thickness. In this case the distances between samples along the trend are taken at 2 to 3 m. The disadvantage of the 'scratch' method is the undesirable excessive comminution of the beryl, which makes it difficult to obtain reliable data on the relationship between the disseminated beryl fraction in the ore and the fraction which can be hand-picked.

The high cost of 'scratch' sampling points to the necessity of recommending its replacement by less expensive sampling methods.

'Scratch' sampling by means of drilling-blasting operations, used in a number of deposits, deserves detailed experimental checking. The blast holes are drilled to a depth of 15 to 20 cm, the size of the charge is computed from the degree of comminution required, without the rock mass being scattered. The width of the 'scratch' samples is assumed in this case to be 1 m, while the length is determined by the thickness of the ore zone. In thick ore zones the section length should not exceed 2 m.

"Grab" Sampling

The problem of the applicability of 'grab' sampling to beryl deposits should be solved in each particular case on the basis of experimental checking. The obstacle to the application of 'grab' sampling can be large dimensions of beryl crystals, characteristic of many pegmatitic deposits. 'Grab' sampling is also not applicable to ore bodies and zones whose thickness is less than the width of the working.

In rare, individual cases the 'grab' method can be recommended in the sampling of thick ore zones characterized by the predominance of small and medium-sized beryl crystals (as much as 5 cm across) and by a relatively high beryl content (more than 0.3 percent). The samples should be taken from the heap after each blasting in the cross-section sampled. The weight of a partial 'grab' sample should not be less than 0.2 kg, while the total weight of the sample of a given heap should be roughly 10 kg.

The most reliable results, as found in the practice of exploration of the beryl deposits, are obtained from the combination of the 'grab' with the 'overall' sampling, which is dealt with below as the 'overall' grab sampling method with ore sorting.

Overall Grab Sampling with Ore Sorting

The suggested method is based on the typical mineralogical feature of most commercial beryl deposits, characterized by the important part played by coarsely-crystalline beryl which lends itself easily to ore-sorting, and on the common rational combination of the exploration of beryl deposits with their tentative mining. When sampling by this method, careful hand picking of beryl is carried out on the rock mass broken down for each gallery or mine working. The beryl yield per 1 m³ of ore zone is determined from the amount of beryl picked and from the accurate measurement of the volume of the working.

Practical experience shows that hand-sorting of the ore makes it possible to pick out all fragments and beryl crystals of over 0.5 cm. The beryllium oxide losses in the tailings after hand-sorting are determined by the parallel grab sampling of tailings and subsequent chemical and mineralogical analyses of the grab samples. The total beryllium oxide content of the sample is determined from the formula:

$$C = \frac{1}{1000} \times \frac{BX}{Y} + II,$$

where C is the total beryllium oxide content of the sample, in percent;
  B is the content of hand-picked beryl in the sample; in kg/m³;
  X is the beryllium oxide content in the picked beryl concentrate according to the results of chemical analysis, in %;
  Y is the specific weight of the ore;
  II is the beryllium oxide content of the tailings after hand-picking, according to the results of chemical analysis, in %.

The cost of the overall grab method differs from that of the grab method only by the cost of the careful picking of beryl ore. The results of the sampling carried out by this method make it possible to get an idea of the amount of beryl which can be extracted from the ore body without using mechanical beneficiation. A favorable feature of the overall grab method with ore sorting is its comparatively low cost and the reliability of obtained relsuts.

The overall grab sampling with ore sorting, conducted during mine pit sinking, enables the preliminary mining of beryl to be organized simultaneously with the exploration of the deposit. As regards the use of this method in large deposits, an obstacle can be found in the multi-sinking of mine workings, which renders more difficult the organization of separate storing of the ore obtained simultaneously from the many faces.

Tentative Sampling During Prospecting for Beryl

The tentative sampling applied during prospection for obtaining a preliminary idea of the limits of content of the useful minerals in the ore body, consists of obtaining by any method (usually by blasting operations), a sufficient quantity of the rock mass and in the subsequent picking of beryl from it, in order to determine the yield of beryl concentrate in kilograms per ton. Simultaneously with beryl-picking, a sample is taken for carrying out chemical and mineralogical analyses for finely disseminated beryl and associated useful minerals. Single samples are usually taken during prospection. The weight of a sample of the finely-disseminated beryllium ores is measured by tens of kilograms, while for the coarse-crystalline beryl ores the weight of the sample should be increased to several hundreds of kilograms.

In the case of good exposures and large sizes of beryl crystals one can recommend graphic sampling which consists in measuring the area of the exposed beryl crystals and calculating the ratio of their total surface area to the area of exposure.

The results of tentative sampling, combined with other geological data, establish the expediency of organizing more detailed work at the deposit site. However, owing to their relative inaccuracy when taken alone they cannot give an idea of the true beryl content in the deposit.

Sampling of Deposits Where Beryllium is an Associated Useful Component (Tungsten, Tin, and Molybdenum Deposits)

In deposits where beryllium minerals are the associated ore-minerals which can be extracted simultaneously with the main ore, the sampling consists of: (1) taking a sufficient number of bulk samples that represent various associations of beryllium minerals (for mineralogical investigation); (2) determining the mean content of beryllium (in beryllium minerals) in the deposit; and (3) establishing the distribution of beryllium (in beryllium minerals) in various portions of the ore-body, and in various types of the main ores.

To obtain the required data for each ore body, horizon, and type of ore, a composite sample is prepared, using the available duplicates of the samples taken for determining the main ore.

Each composite sample is subjected first to a quantitative spectroscopic analysis whose results are used to separate samples with a commercial beryllium content, in order to carry out chemical and mineralogical (immersion) analyses on them. The results of these analyses are used for assessing various ore types, portions of the ore-body, and the entire deposit, and may be used for calculating the resources.

Spacing between Samples

In the exploration of beryl deposits the sampling is carried out along the trend every 2 to 3 m; when the thickness of the ore-body is greater than the cross-section of the working and when it is opened by means of cross-cuts or raises, then the distance between the sampled cuts is increased to 10 to 20 m depending on the geological features of the deposit.

Treatment of Samples

The treatment and concentration of samples of beryl ores are carried out according to the conventional scheme. The greatest difficulty is encountered in the correct choice of the coefficient (K) of the Chechott formula. In a number of cases one has to take into account an excessive complication of the treatment plan, when the coefficient K is sharply increased. Experimental checking in a number of deposits showed that it is expedient to use for the concentration of the samples of beryl ores the Chechott formula with a coefficient K = 0.2 for routine samples and K = 0.4 for control samples. This coefficient can also be applied to the concentration of samples following the preliminary hand-picking of beryl which sharply reduces the irregularity of distribution of the ore-mineral in the remaining ore. When applying preliminary hand-picking of beryl from the sample, one has to concentrate for chemical analysis not only the basic mass of the sample (tailings of hand-picking), but also the picked beryl concentrate. The treatment and concentration of the latter should hardly cause any difficulties, since the treated material may be considered as belonging to the ore type with a very uniform distribution of the beryllium oxide. As the accuracy of chemical analyses of small beryllium oxide contents is, as yet, not very great, the preliminary hand-picking of beryl from the sample makes it possible in a number of cases (especially when the ore is poor in beryl) to avoid the potential errors in the determination of the mean content of beryllium oxide in the sample by the chemical method.

Chemical Analyses

One distinguishes three types of chemical analyses of geological samples for beryllium, each of which characterizes a certain property of the beryl ore under examination.

1. Analyses of the average samples, without previous picking of beryl, determine the gross beryllium oxide content in the ore.

These analyses do not yield a complete idea of the quality of the useful mineral, as they do not give any answer to the question in what form beryllium is present in the ore and how much of it can be extracted by conventional methods of beneficiation. The beryllium oxide content determined in such samples varies within wide limits; for commercial ores they vary from hundredths to tenths of one percent.

2. The analyses of beryl hand-picked from the sample give an idea of the

beryllium oxide content in the beryl concentrate obtained by this simplest method of beneficiation.

In this case the analyst has to deal with the determination of beryllium oxide in the sample between the limits 6 to 13 percent.

3. The analyses of tailings remaining after hand-picking of beryl from the sample determine the sum of beryllium oxide contained in the fine (below 5 mm) fraction of beryllium minerals and of beryllium disseminated in the rock-forming and accessory minerals of the ore zone. The former portion of beryllium can be extracted by mechanical beneficiation methods, while the second, disseminated in other minerals, is practically incapable of extraction. The determination of the extractable part of beryllium remaining in the tailings can be carried out by two methods.

In the direct method determination of the fine fraction of beryl in the sample is made by accurate methods of mineralogical analysis (immersion method). In the indirect method the amount of fine beryl fraction in the sample is calculated by chemical determination of the content of disseminated beryllium in the rock-forming and accessory minerals of the ore zone, followed by a simple calculation

$$K = X - P,$$

where K is the amount of beryllium oxide combined with the fine fraction of beryl or other beryllium minerals in the sample, in percent;

X is the total amount of beryllium oxide in the tailings after hand-picking, in percent;

P is the mean content of beryllium disseminated in the rock-forming and accessory minerals of the ore zone, calculated from the analytical results.

It should be taken into account that, when the mean overall beryllium content of the ore zone is known, it is also necessary to know, in order to evaluate the quality of the ores, its distribution among the fractions that necessitate extraction by various methods of beneficiation. Because the gross beryllium content of the sample can be obtained by totalling the analyses of the beryl picked manually (allowing for the yield) and beryllium remaining in the tailings after hand-picking, the 'mass production' of determinations of the overall beryllium content appears to be inadvisable in exploration tests.

The overall analyses of samples for beryllium can be used for the evaluation of finely disseminated beryllium ores for which the preliminary beneficiation by hand-picking is inapplicable. However, even in this case it is necessary to carry out a mineralogical determination of the content of beryllium minerals in the ore.

The chemical and other analyses should be subjected to internal and external control. The external control should be preferably carried out in laboratories which have experience in 'arbitration' analyses. The external control is indispensable also in cases when the internal control discloses a good convergence of analyses.

Samples for the control are taken so as to contain roughly the same numbers of samples with the average, high, and low content. Each type of ore should be checked separately.

The comparison of analytical data and calculation of errors should be carried out separately for the average, high, and low contents.

The analyses can be considered satisfactory if the mean deviation does not exceed 15 to 25 percent for hundredths of 1 percent, 10 to 15 percent for tenths of 1 percent, and 5 to 10 percent for contents over 1 percent. At the same time the deviations of individual samples should not differ substantially from the above magnitudes, and should be positive and negative.

In addition to chemical analysis, there has been in recent times a more and more widespread application of quantitative spectroscopic and mineralogical analytical methods.

The quantitative spectroscopic analysis is justly applied to the determination of small amounts (0.3–0.0003 percent) of beryllium in minerals and samples. The mineralogical (immersion) analysis, which is a very convenient and sufficiently accurate method, is applied with success to the determination of the beryl content in crushed samples, and of beryl losses in the tailings after the hand-picking of the +5 mm beryl fraction.

Methods of Rating and Grading the Resources into Categories

In order to estimate the resources of beryllium deposits one considers most frequently mining and geological blocks. These methods can be used successfully for both pegmatitic and hydrothermal-pneumatolytic beryllium deposits, represented by ore-bodies whose length considerably exceeds their thickness (veins of various forms, dikes, lenticular bodies).

In individual cases, when grading the resources of vein series and of the stock-shaped and columnar pegmatites with an isometric or irregular outcrop, one is better advised to apply the method of cuts (vertical and horizontal).

The rating of beryllium resources in deposits where beryllium is an accompanying ore-mineral can be carried out by the method of comparison (a modification of the static method).

The advisability of applying any of the rating methods referred to above is determined by the geological features of the deposit and by the degree of its exploration. Thus, the method of mining blocks is expediently applied to the calculation of resources of large ore-bodies of vein form, which will be mined in blocks. By far wider are the possibilities of the method of geological blocks,

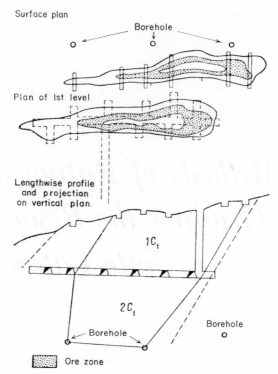

Fig. 40. Exploration of a lenticular pegmatite by a system of mine workings and
boreholes.

applied to the calculation of the resources of various types of beryllium deposits
explored to varying degrees. The method of geological blocks is usually applied
to the calculation of the resources of small ore-bodies which are not required
to be split into mining blocks (Fig. 40). The application of this method can
be also recommended for the rating of the resources of gently-dipping plate-
shaped and veinous bodies open by a system of pits and holes.

The method of vertical cuts can be recommended for the rating of resources
of beryl-bearing vein series characterized by a considerable total extension and
thickness (series of mica-plagioclase or quartz-greisen veins) and explored by a
system of mine workings and boreholes. In this case one determines at each
horizon (in the case of deep boreholes) the ratio of the total thickness of the
individual ore bodies to the total thickness of the series (the coefficient of ore-
content). The calculation is carried out on the basis of the mean total thickness
of ore bodies in the given section.

As an example of the calculation of resources by the method of horizontal
cuts one can quote a thick stock-shaped body explored by mine workings from
the surface and at two levels (see Fig. 22). The areas and the mean contents

of ore zones, calculated on the plans of each level (see Fig. 39) served as the basis for the calculation of resources for each horizontal cut, and then for the blocks between the cuts.

When calculating the beryl resources in deposits where beryl is an accompanying ore-mineral one can use, as mentioned before, the method of comparison. This method can be applied, e.g., for calculating the resources of beryl picked simultaneously when pegmatites are worked for mica. The basis for the calculation of resources in this case may be either the beryl-yield determined per unit volume of the rock mass or the simple ratio of the amount of beryl mined to the amount of the mined main ore-mineral, i.e. muscovite. It should be noted that the resources determined by the method of comparison are only approximate and can be graded only in low categories.

When calculating the resources, a need might arise for introducing correction coefficients: for the irregularity of mineralization (coefficient of ore-content, for barren dikes which transgress the ore body, for the systematic curving of holes, etc.). All these coefficients should be based on sufficient factual material.

Any accessory minerals which have a commercial value must also be calculated. Without this calculation the resources of the main component may not be accepted for exploitation. The calculation of resources of accessory minerals is not obligatory except for deposits with small ore reserves.

Minimum Commercial Beryl Content in Ores

The permissible minimum commercial beryl content of the ores is determined separately for each specific case depending on a number of factors: the scale of the deposit; the mining engineering conditions; the extent of beneficiation of the ores by means of the available methods; the complexity of the ores; the economic conditions of the deposit region.

It is known from the literature that pegmatitic beryl deposits containing 0.2 percent and more of beryl capable of being picked out are worked abroad. It is noted, however, at the same time that, in the case of deposits with less than 0.25 percent of beryl, this mineral can be extracted profitably only together with other useful constituents. In a number of cases one can isolate within one ore-body, a beryl ore-zone proper with a higher beryl content and a complex beryl-spodumene or beryl-tantalite ore-zone where the beryl content may be considerably lower (see Fig. 39). A method of mechanical beneficiation of finely-crystalline beryl, developed recently, should also be taken into account when determining the minimum commercial beryl content of the ore.

The beryllium oxide content of the ore, obtained from the sampling results and used in the calculation of resources, is determined by three components: (1) beryllium oxide in beryl capable of being hand-picked (fraction over 5 mm);

(2) beryllium oxide in finely-crystalline beryl and in beryl excessively comminuted during sampling (fraction below 5 mm), and in small grains of other beryllium-containing minerals which can be extracted into commercial beryllium concentrates by the available methods of mechanical beneficiation; and (3) beryllium oxide disseminated in the rock-forming and accessory minerals of the ore.

The beryllium oxide in the beryl fraction over 5 mm can be extracted by hand-picking. To extract the beryl fraction of less than 5 mm as well as other beryllium minerals extracted in the concentrate, it is necessary to apply mechanical beneficiation methods. Beryllium disseminated in the rock-forming and accessory minerals of the ore-zone is practically non-extractable.

Mapping of Ore Zones

The mapping of the boundaries of ore-zones in the hydrothermal-pneumatolytic vein beryl deposits can be carried out by the usual method on the basis of the sampling results. In a number of cases, when resources are calculated for a rather thin beryl-bearing vein or a streak with a high beryl concentration, one takes into account the working thickness of the excavated space (0.7 to 0.8 m when the ore-bodies are steeply-dipping, 1 to 1.2 m when they are gently-dipping). It is expedient to calculate the excavated space in cases where it is obviously impossible to carry out a separate excavation of the ore-body and to avoid losses in ore-fines when the ore is being excavated. In a number of cases, when the boundaries of the ore-zones are mapped in pegmatitic beryl deposits, a close relationship between beryl and certain texture-paragenetical features is very helpful. In such cases the boundaries of the ore-zone are determined by the boundaries of the beryl-bearing paragenetical complex and can be established during the detailed mapping of the pegmatite.

Grading of Resources by Categories

The grading of resources of beryl deposits by categories is carried out in accordance with the instruction of GKZ (Government Commission for Mineral Resources). It should be taken into account that some beryl deposits of all types belong to groups "C" and "D" of the instruction referred to above, and therefore the resources of beryl deposits are not graded in categories A_1 and A_2.

One can refer to category B the resources of beryl deposits of the group "C" within normal blocks explored from three or four sides by mine workings and separated from each other along the dip by not more than the height of the exploitation storey (30 to 40 m).

When referring resources to category B, one has to observe the following conditions:

1. elucidation of the form of the ore-body and of the distribution of the natural types, volume and mass [weight in tons] of the ores with an accuracy fully sufficient to effect a reliable calculation of resources for the entire ore-body;

2. presence of detailed geological plans of pegmatites on the scale 1/100–1/500 (depending on the dimensions of ore-bodies), in which the paragenetical complexes of the pegmatites are delineated;

3. availability of sufficiently complete information on the mineralogical and chemical composition of the ores, on the nature and size of crystals and grains of beryllium minerals, on the beryllium oxide content of the rock-forming and accessory minerals of ore-zones;

4. determination (in percent) of the degree of extraction and of the extent of losses of beryllium oxide for the available beneficiation methods;

5. continuous sampling of thick ore zones by means of workings which intersect the zones across their trend with a sufficient density of crosscuts; in rather thin ore-bodies which do not exceed the boundaries of the working and which are tested by sampling along the drive or the lengthwise trench, the sample spacing should not exceed 2 to 3 m;

6. for deposits with an irregular (pocket-type or columnar) distribution of mineralization, and given conditions which make it possible to leave the barren portions in pillars and to remove them during ore sorting, one has to calculate the reliable coefficient of ore-bearing capacity for each block; and

7. technological properties of ores (possible degree of beneficiation) should be studied on representative samples in industrial or semi-industrial conditions.

The absence of information on technological tests or their unsatisfactory results may be considered as the reason for lowering the category of resources or for a temporary refusal of their being approved.

Besides the circumstances referred to above, the ore resources graded as category B should satisfy all other requirements made in the GKZ instruction with regard to this category.

One can refer to category C_1 the beryllium resources of deposits opened and tested by sampling only from the surface with a sufficient density of the exploration network, and resources which are presumed to exist on the basis of a sparse network of exploratory workings beyond the boundaries of blocks explored in detail and referred to category B. Besides, to category C_1 belong beryllium resources explored by deep holes, provided these resources, based on the cores, are from a sampled surface or a sampled horizon of the ore-body, or from B-category blocks; for pegmatites the indispensable condition is the absence of a sharp zonal change and of variability of ore-content along the section.

When referring beryllium resources to category C_1 one has to observe the following conditions:

1. elucidation in general terms of the shape, dimensions, and nature of occurrence of the ore-body;

2. calculation of the volume and mass of ore within the limits of the conventional outline on the network of exploratory workings, or by way of limited extrapolation beyond the outline of exploratory workings; in pegmatitic deposits the extrapolation along the trend is permissible only if the zonation entitles one to expect that the ore-bearing paragenetical complex extends beyond the explored boundary;

3. extrapolation in depth for a distance not exceeding one-fourth of the length of the ore body; the depth of extrapolation along the vertical should not exceed one exploitation storey (30 to 40 m); extrapolation in depth in pegmatitic deposits is inadmissible if it is known that the zonation of the pegmatite changes abruptly with depth;

4. availability of geological plans of pegmatites on the scale 1/200 to 1/500 (depending on the dimensions of the body), on which the paragenetical complexes-zones are diagrammatically delineated;

5. availability of previous information on the mineralogical and chemical composition of the ores, on the nature and size of the crystals and grains of beryllium minerals;

6. approximate determination of the beryllium oxide losses in the currently-used beneficiation methods; and

7. technological properties of the ore should be known in analogy to other well-studied deposits, or tested in laboratory conditions.

The coefficient of ore-bearing content and other correction coefficients for the resources of category C_1 may be introduced not for every block, but for the entire ore-body.

The ore resources graded in category C_1 should satisfy all other conditions set forth in the GKZ instruction with regard to the category in question.

To category C_2 there are referred resources of beryllium deposits, which adjoin the blocks explored in category C_1, given the geological data which entitle one to expect that the beryl-bearing ore-zone extends beyond the boundaries of the resources of higher categories.

One can also refer to category C_2 the resources of deposits, calculated on the basis of single samples, when the diagrammatic plan of the ore body is available.

References

Adams, J. W. (1953), Beryllium deposits of the Mount Antero region, Chaffee county, Colorado, U.S. Geol. Surv. Bull. No. 982-D.

Barlow, N. E., G. Kh. Spector, and D. F. Brown (1955), Field determination of beryl (Polevoe opredelenie berilla), Symposium "Berillii," edited by A. A. Beus and M. B. Reifman, *Izd. inostr. lit.* Issue 3.

Beus, A. A. (1951), Zonation of granitic pegmatites (O zonal'nosti granitnykh pegmatitov), *Izv. Akad. Nauk SSSR*, ser. geol., No. 6.

———— (1953), Isomorphism of beryllium in connection with phenomena of its concentration and dissemination (Ob izonorfizme berilliya v svyazi s yavleniyami ego kontsentratsii i rasseyaniya), *Dokl. Akad. Nauk SSSR*, new series, vol. 90, No. 3.

———— (1954), Problem of the origin of zonation in granitic pegmatites (K voprosu o proiskhozhdenii zonal'nosti granitnykh pegmatitov), *Dokl. Akad. Nauk SSSR*, new series, vol. 97, No. 1.

———— (1955), The mean beryllium content (clarke) of granitic pegmatites (O klarke berilliya v granitnykh pegmatitakh), *Dokl. Akad. Nauk SSSR*, new series, vol. 104, No. 1.

———— (1956a), Beryllium - Valuation of deposits in exploration and prospecting (Berillii-Otsenka mestorozhdenii pri poiskakh i razvedkakh), *Gosgeoltekhizdat.*

———— (1956b), On beryllium vesuvianite (O berillievom vesuviane), *Trudy Mineralogicheskogo muzeya Acad. Nauk SSSR (Transactions of the Mineralogical Museum, Academy of Sciences USSR)*, vol. 8.

———— (1956c), Characteristics of diadochic entry of beryllium into crystal structures of minerals (Osobennosti izomorfnogo vkhozhdeniya berilliya v kristallicheskuyu strukturu mineralov), *Geokhimiya*, vol. 1, No. 67.

———— and N. E. Zalashkova (1956d), On the genesis of sodium beryl in pegmatites (O genezise natrievoi modifikatsii berilla v pegmatitakh): Mineralogicheskii sbornik L'vovskogo geologich. ob-va (Mineralogical Collection, L'vov Geological Society), No. 10.

Brandenberger, E. (1932), Die Kristallstruktur von Beryllium fluorid, *Schweiz, min. u. petrog. Mitteilung*, vol. 12, No. 243.

Cameron, E. N., and V. E. Shainin (1947), The beryl resources of Connecticut, *Econ. Geology*, vol. 42, No. 4.

————, R. H. Jahns, A. H. McNair, and L. R. Page (1951), Internal structure of granitic pegmatites (Vnutrennee stroenie granitnykh pegmatitov). *Izd. iinostr. lit.; Econ. Geology*, Mon. 2, 115 p., 1949.

Cameron, E. N., R. B. Rowe, and P. L. Weiss (1953), Fluid inclusions in beryl and quartz from pegmatites of the Middletown district, Connecticut, *Am. Mineralogist*, vol. 38, No. 3–4.

Dorfman, M. D. (1952), Determination of the genesis of beryl (K voprosu opredeleniya genezisa berilla). *Dokl. Akad. Nauk SSSR*, vol. 82, No. 4.

Fersman, A. E. (1936–1939), Geochemistry (Geokhimiya), I–IV, Academy of Sciences USSR Press.

――― (1940), Pegmatites (Pegmatity), Academy of Sciences USSR Press.

Goldschmidt, V. M., and K. K. Peters (1938), Geochemistry of beryllium (K geokhimii berilliya). Symposium of articles on rare elements. *Izd. inostr. lit.*, Academy of Sciences USSR Press.

Ginzburg, A. I. (1949), Prospecting criteria of rare-metal pegmatites (Poiskovye priznaki redkometal'nykh pegmatitov). *Razvedka Nedr*, No. 3.

――― (1955), On the chemical composition of beryl (K voprosu o khimicheskom sostave berilla). *Trudy Mineralogicheskogo muzeya Acad. Nauk SSSR (Transactions of the Mineralogical Museum, Academy of Sciences USSR)*, No. 7.

Hill, W. U. (1934), Structure of vitreous BeF_2, *Zt. Kryst.* (A), vol. 89, No. 481.

Holser, W. T. (1953), Beryllium minerals in the Victorio Mountains, Luna County, New Mexico. *Amer. Mineralogist*, vol. 38; Nos. 7/8.

Jahns, R. H. (1944), Ribbon Rock an unusual beryllium-bearing tactite. *Econ. Geology*, vol. 39; No. 3.

Kosov, B. M., and N. M. Ostromenetskii (1949), Valuation of deposits during prospection and exploration (Otsenka mestorozhdenii pri poiskakh i razvedkakh), *Gosgeolizdat*, No. 2, Tin (Olovo).

Minerals Yearbook, 1940–1952, U.S. Bur. of Mines.

Nikol'skii, A. P. (1954), Prospecting for minerals during geological survey work. Tungsten deposits. Methodical handbook of geological survey and prospection of VSEGEI (Poiski poleznykh iskopaemykh pri geologo-s'emochnykh rabotakh. Mestorozhdeniya vol'frama. Metodicheskoe rukovodstvo po feologicheskoi s'emke i poiskam VSEGEI). *Gosgeoltekhizdat*.

Resources for Freedom, 1952. A report to the President by the President's Materials Policy Commission.

Petrov, V. P. and N. V. Lizunov (1946), Content of trace elements in the Urals refractory clays and kaolins (Soderzhanie mikroelementov v ural'skikh ogneupornykh glinakh i kaolinakh). Symposium: Voprosy mineralogii, geokhimii i petrografii. *Akad. Nauk SSSR*.

Rankama, K. and Th. Sahama (1950), *Geochemistry*, Chicago.

Sandell, E. B. (1952), Beryllium content of igneous rocks, *Geochim. et Cosmochim.* Acta vol. 2, p. 211.

Smirnov, V. I. (1954), Geological foundations of prospecting for and exploring ore deposits (Geologicheskie osnovy poiskov i razvedok rudnykh mestorozhdenii), MGU.

Sobolev, V. S. (1949), Introduction to the mineralogy of silicates (Vvedenie v mineralogiyu silikatov), University of L'vov Press.

Solov'ev, S. P. (1952), Distribution of igneous rocks in the USSR (Respredelenie magmaticheskikh gornykh porod v SSSR), *Gosgeolizdat*.

Vol'fson, F. I. (1954), Structures of endogenous ore deposits (Struktury endogennykh rudnykh mestorozhdenii). Symposium "Fundamental problems in the theory of magmatogenous ore deposits" (Osnovnye problemy v uchenii o magmatogennyk rudnykh nestorozhdenivakh). *Akad. Nauk SSSR.*

Vinogradov, A. P. (1950), Geochemistry of the rare and disseminated elements in soils (Geokhimiya redkikh i rasseyannykh elementov v pochvakh).

Vlasov, K. A. (1938a), Catalytic role of fluorine in the process of desilication of pegmatite and genesis of beryl (Kataliticheskaya rol'ftora v protsesse desilikatsii pegmatita i genezisa berilla). *Trudy Lomonosovskogo Instituta Akad. Nauk SSSR,* No. IX.

―――― (1938b), Theory of desilication of granitic pegmatites (O teorii desilikatsii granitnykh pegmatitov). *Izv. Akad. Nauk SSSR,* ser. geol., No. 2.

―――― (1943), Significance of forms of granitic pegmatites (Znachenie form granitnykh pegmatitov). *Dokl. Akad. Nauk SSSR,* vol. 41, No. 9.

―――― (1952), Texture-paragenetical classification of granitic pegmatites (Teksturno-paragenticheskaya klassifikatsiya granitnykh pegmatitov). *Izv. Akad. Nauk SSSR,* ser. geol., No. 2.

Index